SOLUTIONS MANUAL

Second Edition

Data Networks

DIMITRI BERTSEKAS

Massachusetts Institute of Technology

ROBERT GALLAGER

Massachusetts Institute of Technology

PRENTICE HALL, Upper Saddle River, New Jersey 07458

© 1993 Prentice-Hall, Inc.
A Pearson Education Company
Upper Saddle River, NJ 07458

Printed in the United States of America

12

ISBN 0-13-200924-2

Prentice-Hall International (UK) Limited,London
Prentice-Hall of Australia Pty. Limited, Sydney
Prentice-Hall Canada Inc., Toronto
Prentice-Hall Hispanoamericana, S.A., Mexico
Prentice-Hall of India Private Limited, New Delhi
Prentice-Hall of Japan, Inc., Tokyo
Pearson Education Asia Pte. Ltd., Singapore
Editora Prentice-Hall do Brasil, Ltda., Rio de Janeiro

Solutions Manual -- <u>Data Networks, 2/E</u> by Dimitri Bertsekas and Robert Gallager

TABLE OF CONTENTS

ACKNOWLEDGMENTS

Several of our students have contributed to this solutions manual. We are particularly thankful to Rajesh Pankaj, Jane Simmons, John Spinelli, and Manos Varvarigos.

CHAPTER 1 SOLUTIONS

1.1

There are 250,000 pixels per square inch, and multiplying by the number of square inches and the number of bits per pixel gives 5.61×10^8 bits.

1.2

a) There are 16×10^9 bits going into the network per hour. Thus there are 48×10^9 bits per hour traveling through the network, or 13.33 million bits per second. This requires 209 links of 64 kbit/sec. each.

b) Since a telephone conversation requires two people, and 10% of the people are busy on the average, we have 50,000 simultaneous calls on the average, which requires 150,000 links on the average. Both the answer in a) and b) must be multiplied by some factor to provide enough links to avoid congestion (and to provide local access loops to each telephone), but the point of the problem is to illustrate how little data, both in absolute and comparative terms, is required for ordinary data transactions by people.

1.3

There are two possible interpretations of the problem. In the first, packets can be arbitrarily delayed or lost and can also get out of order in the network. In this interpretation, if a packet from A to B is sent at time τ and not received by some later time t, there is no way to tell whether that packet will ever arrive later. Thus if any data packet or protocol packet from A to B is lost, node B can never terminate with the assurance that it will never receive another packet.

In the second interpretation, packets can be arbitrarily delayed or lost, but cannot get out of order. Assume that each node is initially in a communication state, exchanging data packets. Then each node, perhaps at different times, goes into a state or set of states in which it sends protocol packets in an attempt to terminate. Assume that a node can enter the final termination state only on the receipt of one of these protocol packets (since timing information cannot help, since there is no side information, and since any data packet could be followed by another data packet). As in the three army problem, assume any particular ordering in which the two nodes receive protocol packets. The first node to receive a protocol packet cannot go to the final termination state since it has no assurance that any protocol packet will ever be received by the other node, and thus no assurance that the other node will ever terminate. The next protocol packet to be received then finds neither node in the final termination state. Thus again the receiving node cannot terminate without the possibility that the other node will receive no more protocol packets and thus never terminate. The same situation occurs on each received protocol packet, and thus it is impossible to guarantee that both nodes can eventually terminate. This is essentially the same argument as used for the three army problem.

CHAPTER 2 SOLUTIONS

2.1

Let x(t) be the output for the single pulse shown in Fig. 2.3(a) and let y(t) be the output for the sequence of pulses in Fig. 2.3(b). The input for 2.3(b) is the sum of six input pulses of the type in 2.3(a); the first such pulse is identical to that of 2.3(a), the second is delayed by T time units, the third is inverted and delayed by 2T time units, etc. From the time invariance property, the response to the second pulse above is x(t-T) (i.e. x(t) delayed by T); from the time invariance and linearity, the response to the third pulse is -x(t-2T). Using linearity to add the responses to the six pulses, the overall output is

$$y(t) = x(t) + x(t\text{-}T) - x(t\text{-}2T) + x(t\text{-}3T) - x(t\text{-}4T) - x(t\text{-}5T)$$

To put the result in more explicit form, note that

$$x(t) = \begin{cases} 0 & ; \quad t < 0 \\ 1 - e^{-2t/T} & ; \quad 0 \le t < T \\ (e^2 - 1)e^{-2t/T} & ; \quad t \ge T \end{cases}$$

Thus the response from the ith pulse ($1 \le i \le 6$) is zero up to time (i-1)T. For t < 0, then, y(t) = 0; from $0 \le t < T$

$$y(t) = x(t) = 1 - e^{-2t/T} \quad ; \ 0 \le t < T$$

From $T \le t < 2T$,

$$y(t) = x(t) + x(t\text{-}T)$$

$$= (e2\text{ -}1)e^{-2t/T} + [1 - e^{-2(t\text{-}T)/T}]$$

$$= 1 - e^{-2t/T}$$

Similarly, for $2T \le t < 3T$,

$$y(t) = x(t) + x(t\text{-}T) - x(t\text{-}2T)$$

$$= (e^2\text{-}1)e^{-2t/T} + (e^2\text{-}1)e^{-2(t\text{-}T)/T} - [1 - e^{-2(t\text{-}2T)/T}]$$

$$= -1 + (2e^4\text{-}1)e^{-2t/T} \quad ; \ 2T \le t < 3T$$

A similar analysis for each subsequent interval leads to

$$y(t) = 1 - (2e^6 - 2e^4 + 1)e^{-2t/T} \quad ; \quad 3T \le t < 4T$$

$$= -1 + (2e^8 - 2e^6 + 2e^4 - 1)e^{-2t/T} \quad ; \quad 4T \le t < 6T$$

$$= -(e^{12} - 2e^8 + 2e^6 - 2e^4 + 1)e^{-2t/T} \quad ; \quad t \ge 6T$$

The solution is continuous over t with slope discontinuities at 0, 2T, 3T, 4T, and 6T; the value of y(t) at these points is y(0) = 0; y(2T) = .982; y(3T) = -.732; y(4T) = .766; y(6T) = -.968.   Another approach to the problem that gets the solution with less work is to use x(t) to first find the response to a unit step and then view y(t) as the response to a sum of displaced unit steps.

2.2

From the convolution equation, Eq. (2.1), the output r(t) is

$$r(t) = \int_{-\infty}^{\infty} s(\tau)h(t-\tau)d\tau = \int_{\tau=0}^{T} h(t-\tau)d\tau$$

Note that $h(t-\tau) = \alpha e^{-\alpha(t-\tau)}$ for $t-\tau \geq 0$, (i.e. for $\tau \leq t$), and $h(t-\tau) = 0$ for $\tau > t$. Thus for t < 0, $h(t-\tau) = 0$ throughout the integration interval above. For $0 \leq t < T$, we then have

$$r(t) = \int_{\tau=0}^{t} \alpha e^{-\alpha(t-\tau)}d\tau + \int_{\tau=t}^{T} 0\,d\tau\ = 1 - e^{-\alpha t}\quad ; 0 \leq t < T$$

For $t \geq T$, $h(t-\tau) = \alpha e^{-\alpha(t-\tau)}$ over the entire integration interval and

$$r(t) = \int_{\tau=0}^{T} \alpha e^{-\alpha(t-\tau)}d\tau\ = e^{-\alpha(t-T)} - e^{-\alpha t}\quad ; t \geq T$$

Thus the response increases towards 1 for $0 \leq t \leq T$ with the exponential decay factor α, and then, for $t \geq T$, decays toward 0.

2.3

From Eq. (2.1),

$$r(t) = \int_{-\infty}^{\infty} e^{j2\pi f\tau}h(t-\tau)d\tau$$

Using $\tau' = t-\tau$ as the variable of integration for any given t,

$$r(t) = \int_{-\infty}^{\infty} e^{j2\pi f(t-\tau')}h(\tau')d\tau'$$

$$= e^{j2\pi ft}\int_{-\infty}^{\infty} e^{-j2\pi f\tau'}h(\tau')d\tau'$$

$$= e^{j2\pi ft}H(f)$$

where H(f) is as given in Eq. (2.3).

2.4

$$h(t) = \int_{-\infty}^{+\infty} H(f)e^{j2\pi ft}df$$

Since $H(f)$ is 1 from $-f_0$ to f_0 and 0 elsewhere, we can integrate $\exp(j2\pi ft)$ from $-f_0$ to f_0, obtaining

$$h(t) = \frac{1}{j2\pi t}[\exp(j2\pi f_0 t) - \exp(-i2\pi f_0 t)] = \frac{\sin(2\pi f_0 t)}{\pi t}$$

Note that this impulse response is unrealizable in the sense that the response starts before the impulse (and, even worse, starts an infinite time before the impulse). None the less, such ideal filters are useful abstractions in practice.

2.5

The function $s_1(t)$ is compressed by a factor of β on the time axis as shown below

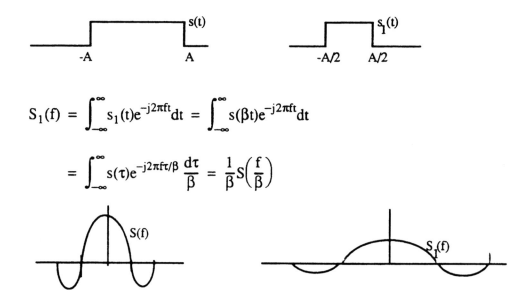

$$S_1(f) = \int_{-\infty}^{\infty} s_1(t)e^{-j2\pi ft}dt = \int_{-\infty}^{\infty} s(\beta t)e^{-j2\pi ft}dt$$

$$= \int_{-\infty}^{\infty} s(\tau)e^{-j2\pi f\tau/\beta}\frac{d\tau}{\beta} = \frac{1}{\beta}S\left(\frac{f}{\beta}\right)$$

Thus $S_1(f)$ is attenuated by a factor of β in amplitude and expanded by a factor of β on the frequency scale; compressing a function in time expands it in frequency and vice versa.

2.6

a) We use the fact that $\cos(x) = [\exp(jx) + \exp(-jx)]/2$. Thus the Fourier transform of $s(t)\cos(2\pi f_0 t)$ is

$$\int_{-\infty}^{\infty} s(t)\frac{\exp(j2\pi f_0 t) + \exp(-j2\pi f_0 t)}{2}\exp(-j2\pi ft)\,dt$$

$$= \frac{s(t)}{2}\exp[-j2\pi(f-f_0)t]\,dt + \frac{s(t)}{2}\exp[-j2\pi(f+f_0)t]\,dt$$

$$= \frac{S(f-f_0)}{2} + \frac{S(f+f_0)}{2}$$

b) Here we use the identity $\cos^2(x) = [1+\cos(2x)]/2$. Thus the Fourier transform of $s(t)\cos^2(2pf_0t)$ is the Fourier transform of $s(t)/2$ plus the Fourier transform of $s(t)\cos[2p(2f_0)t]/2$. Using the result in part a, this is $S(f)/2 + S(f-2f_0)/4 + S(f+2f_0)/4$.

2.7

a) E{frame time on 9600 bps link} = 1000 bits / 9600 bps = 0.104 sec.

   E{frame time on 50,000bps link} = 0.02 sec.

b) E{time for 10^6 frames on 9600 bps link} = $1.04 \cdot 10^5$ sec.

   E{time for 10^6 frames on 50,000 bps link} = $2 \cdot 10^4$ sec.

Since the frame lengths are statistically independent, the variance of the total number of bits in 10^6 frames is 10^6 times the variance for one frame. Thus the standard deviation of the total number of bits in 10^6 frames is 10^3 times the standard deviation of the bits in one frame or $5 \cdot 10^5$ bits. The standard deviation of the transmission time is then

   S.D.{time for 10^6 frames on 9600 bps link} = $5 \cdot 10^5 / 9600 = 52$ sec.

   S.D.{time for 10^6 frames on 50,000 bps link} = $5 \cdot 10^5 / 50,000 = 10$ sec.

c) The point of all the above calculations is to see that, for a large number of frames, the expected time to transmit the frames is very much larger than the standard deviation of the transmission time; that is, the time per frame, averaged over a very long sequence of frames, is close to the expected frame time with high probability. One's intuition would then suggest that the number of frames per unit time, averaged over a very long time period, is close to the reciprocal of the expected frame time with high probability. This intuition is correct and follows either from renewal theory or from direct analysis. Thus the reciprocal of the expected frame time is the rate of frame transmissions in the usual sense of the word "rate".

2.8

Let x_{ij} be the bit in row i, column j. Then the ith horizontal parity check is

$$h_i = \Sigma_j \, x_{ij}$$

where the summation is summation modulo 2. Summing both sides of this equation (modulo 2) over the rows i, we have

$$\Sigma_i \, h_i = \Sigma_{i,j} \, x_{ij}$$

This shows that the modulo 2 sum of all the horizontal parity checks is the same as the modulo 2 sum of all the data bits. The corresponding argument on columns shows that the modulo 2 sum of the vertical parity checks is the same.

2.9

a) Any pattern of the form

$$--- 1\ 1\ 0 ---$$
$$--- 0\ 1\ 1 ---$$
$$--- 1\ 0\ 1 ---$$

will fail to be detected by horizontal and vertical parity checks. More formally, for any three rows i_1, i_2, and i_3, and any three columns j_1, j_2, and j_3, a pattern of six errors in positions $(i_1\ j_1)$, $(i_1\ j_2)$, $(i_2\ j_2)$, $(i_2\ j_3)$, $(i_3\ j_1)$, and $(i_3\ j_3)$ will fail to be detected.

b) The four errors must be confined to two rows, two errors in each, and to two columns, two errors in each; that is, geometrically, they must occur at the vertices of a rectangle within the array. Assuming that the data part of the array is J by K, then the array including the parity check bits is J+1 by K+1. There are $(J+1)J/2$ different possible pairs of rows (counting the row of vertical parity checks), and $(K+1)K/2$ possible pairs of columns (counting the column of horizontal checks). Thus there are $(J+1)(K+1)JK/4$ undetectable patterns of four errors.

2.10

Let $x = (x_1, x_2, \dots x_N)$ and $x' = (x'_1, x'_2, \dots x'_N)$ be any two distinct code words in a parity check code. Here $N = K+L$ is the length of the code words (K data bits plus L check bits). Let $y = (y_1, \dots y_N)$ be any given binary string of length N. Let $D(x,y)$ be the distance between x and y (i.e. the number of positions i for which $x_i \neq y_i$). Similarly let $D(x',y)$ and $D(x,x')$ be the distances between x' and y and between x and x'. We now show that

$$D(x,x') \leq D(x,y) + D(x',y)$$

To see this, visualize changing $D(x,y)$ bits in x to obtain y, and then changing $D(x',y)$ bits in y to obtain x'. If no bit has been changed twice in going from x to y and then to x', then it was necessary to change $D(x,y) + D(x',y)$ bits to change x to x' and the above inequality is satisfied with equality. If some bits have been changed twice (i.e. $x_i = x'_i \neq y_i$ for some i) then strict inequality holds above.

By definition of the minimum distance d of a code, $D(x,x') \geq d$. Thus, using the above inequality, if $D(x,y) < d/2$, then $D(x',y) > d/2$. Now suppose that code word x is sent and fewer than d/2 errors occur. Then the received string y satisfies $D(x,y) < d/2$ and for every other code word x', $D(x',y) > d/2$. Thus a decoder that maps y into the closest code word must select x, showing that no decoding error can be made if fewer than d/2 channel errors occur. Note that this argument applies to any binary code rather than just parity check codes.

2.11

The first code word given, 1001011 has only the first data bit equal to 1 and has the first, third, and fourth parity checks equal to 1. Thus those parity checks must check on the first data bit. Similarly, from the second code word, we see that the first, second, and fourth parity checks must check on the second bit. From the third code word, the first, second, and third parity check each check on the third data bit. Thus

$$c_1 = s_1 + s_2 + s_3$$
$$c_2 = s_2 + s_3$$
$$c_3 = s_1 + s_3$$
$$c_4 = s_1 + s_2$$

The set of all code words is given by

0000000	0011110
1001011	1010101
0101101	0110011
1100110	1111000

The minimum distance of the code is 4, as can be seen by comparing all pairs of code words. An easier way to find the minimum distance of a parity check code is to observe that if x and x' are each code words, then x + x' (using modulo 2 componentwise addition) is also a code word. On the other hand, x + x' has a 1 in a position if and only if x and x' differ in that position. Thus the distance between x and x' is the number of ones in x + x'. It follows that the minimum distance of a parity check code is the minimum, over all non-zero code words, of the number of ones in each code word.

2.12

$$
\begin{array}{r}
D^3 \\
D^4 + D^2 + D + 1 \overline{)\ D^7 + D^5 + D^4} \\
\underline{D^7 + D^5 + D^4 + D^3} \\
D^3 \quad = \text{Remainder}
\end{array}
$$

2.13

Let $z(D) = D^j + z_{j-1}D^{j-1} + \ldots + D^i$ and assume $i < j$. Multiplying G(D) times Z(D) then yields

$$g(D)z(D) = D^{L+j} + (z_{j-1} + g_{L-1})D^{L+j-1} + (z_{j-2} + g_{L-1}z_{j-1} + g_{L-2})D^{L+j-2} + \ldots$$
$$+ (g_1 + z_{i+1})D^{i+1} + D^i$$

Clearly the coefficient of D^{L+j} and the coefficient of D^i are each 1, yielding the desired two non-zero terms. The above case $i < j$ arises whenever z(D) has more than one non-zero term. For the case in which z(D) has only one non-zero term, i.e. $z(D) = Dj$ for some j, we have

$$g(D)z(D) = D^{L+j} + g_{L-1}D^{L+j-1} + \ldots + D^j$$

which again has at least two non-zero terms.

2.14

Suppose g(D) contains (1+D) as a factor; thus g(D) = (1+D)h(D) for some polynomial h(D). Substituting 1 for D and evaluating with modulo 2 arithmetic, we get g(1) = 0 because of the term (1+D) = (1+1) = 0. Let e(D) be the polynomial for some arbitrary undetectable error sequence. Then e(D) = g(D)z(D) for some z(D), and hence e(1) = g(1)z(1) = 0. Now $e(D) = \sum_i e_i D^i$, so $e(1) = \sum_i e_i$. Thus e(1) = 0 implies that an even number of elements e_i

are 1; i.e. that $e(D)$ corresponds to an even number of errors. Thus all undetectable error sequences contain an even number of errors; any error sequence with an odd number of errors is detected.

2.15

a) Let D^{i+L}, divided by $g(D)$, have the quotient $z^{(i)}(D)$ and remainder $c^{(i)}(D)$ so that

$$D^{i+L} = g(D)z^{(i)}(D) + c^{(i)}(D)$$

Multiplying by s_i and summing over i,

$$s(D)D^L = \Sigma_i\, s_i z^{(i)}(D) + \Sigma_i\, s_i c^{(i)}(D)$$

Since $\Sigma_i\, s_i c^{(i)}(D)$ has degree less than L, this must be the remainder (and $\Sigma_i\, s_i z^{(i)}(D)$ the quotient) on dividing $s(D)D^L$ by $g(D)$. Thus $c(D) = \Sigma_i\, s_i c^{(i)}(D)$.

b) Two polynomials are equal if and only if their coefficients are equal, so the above polynomial equality implies

$$c_j = \Sigma_i\, s_i c_j^{(i)}$$

2.16

a) Consider the two scenarios below and note that these scenarios are indistinguishable to the receiver.

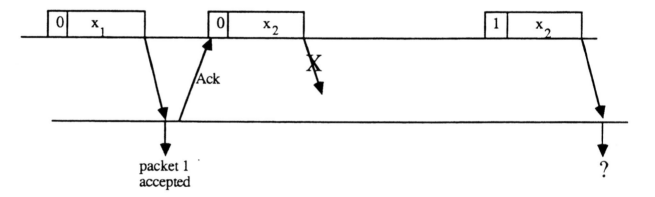

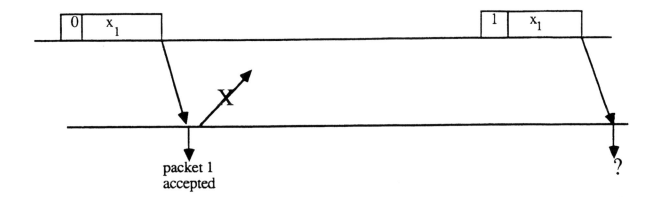

If the receiver releases the packet as x_2 in the questioned reception, then an error occurs on scenario 2. If the receiver returns an ack but doesn't release a packet (i.e. the appropriate action for scenario 2), then under scenario 1, the transmitter erroneously goes on to packet 3. Finally, if the receiver returns a nak, the problem is only postponed since the transmitter would then transmit $(2,x_2)$ in scenario 1 and $(2,x_1)$ in scenario 2. As explained on page 66, packets x_1 and x_2 might be identical bit strings, so the receiver can not resolve its ambiguity by the bit values of the packets.

b) The scenarios below demonstrate incorrect operation for the modified conditions.

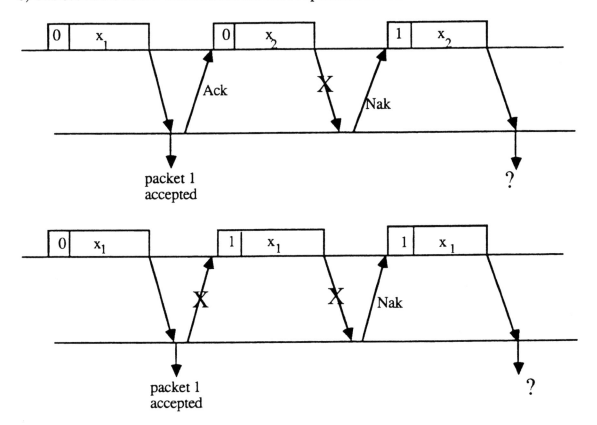

2.17

a) $\quad T = T_t + T_f + 2T_d$

b) $\quad q = (1-p_t)(1-p_f)$

A packet is transmitted once with probability q, twice with probability (1-q)q, three times with probability $(1-q)^2q$, etc. Thus the expected number of transmissions of a given packet is

$$E\{\text{transmissions per packet}\} = \sum_{i=1}^{\infty} iq(1-q)^{i-1} = \frac{1}{q}$$

To verify the above summation, note that for any x, $0 \le x < 1$,

$$\sum_{i=1}^{\infty} ix^{i-1} = \sum_{i=1}^{\infty} \frac{dx^i}{dx} = \frac{d}{dx}\sum_{i=1}^{\infty} x^i = \frac{d}{dx}\left(\frac{x}{1-x}\right) = \frac{1}{(1-x)^2}$$

Using x for (1-q) above gives the desired result.

c) $\quad E\{\text{time per packet}\} = (T_t + T_f + 2T_d)/q$

$$= (1.3)/0.998 = 1.303$$

Note that p_t and p_f have very little effect on E[time per packet] in stop and wait systems unless they are unusually large.

2.18

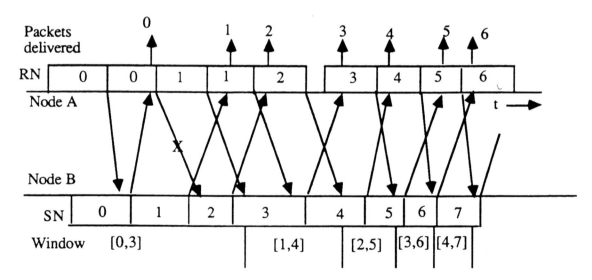

Assume that the transmitter always sends the next packet in order until reaching the end of the window, and then goes back to the beginning of the window.

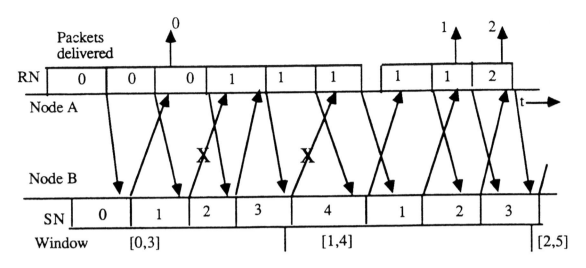

2.19

The simplest such deadlock occurs if there is sufficient propagation delay in the system that each side can send n-1 frames (containing packets numbered 0 to n-2) before finishing receipt of the first frame from the other side. In this case, the nth frame from each side will carry the packet numbered n-1 without acking any packets from the other side. Thus each side will go back to packet 0, but in the absence of errors, each side will be looking for packet n by time the repeat of packet 0 occurs. Each side will then cycle from 0 to n-1, and neither side will ever receive any acks. The diagram below illustrates this for n=3. The first number in each frame position is SN and the second is RN.

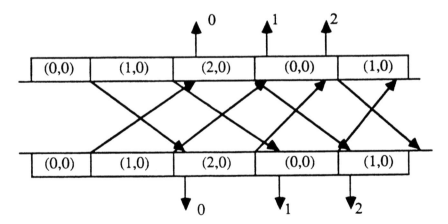

2.20

The simplest example is for node A to send packets 0 through n-1 in the first n frames. In case of delayed acknowledgements (i.e. no return packets in the interim), node A goes back and retransmits packet 0. If the other node has received all the packets, it is waiting for packet n, and if the modulus m equals n, this repeat of packet 0 is interpreted as packet n.

The right hand side of Eq. (2.24) is satisfied with equality if $SN = SN_{min}(t_1)+n-1$. This occurs if node A sends packets 0 through $n-1$ in the first n frames with no return packets from node B. The last such frame has $SN = n-1$, whereas SN_{min} at that time (say t_1) is 0.

Continuing this scenario, we find an example where the right hand side of Eq. (2.25) is satisfied with equality. If all the frames above are correctly received, then after the last frame, RN becomes equal to n. If another frame is sent from A (now call this time t_1) and if SN_{min} is still 0, then when it is received at B (say at t_2), we have $RN(t_2) = SN_{min}(t_1)+n$.

2.21

Let $RN(\tau)$ be the value of RN at node B at an arbitrary time τ; SN_{min} is the smallest packet number not yet acknowledged at A at time t (which is regarded as fixed) and $SN_{max}-1$ is the largest packet number sent from A at time t. Since $RN(\tau)$ is non decreasing in τ, it is sufficient to show that $RN(t+T_m+T_d) \le SN_{max}$ and to show that $RN(t-T_m-T_d) \ge SN_{min}$.

For the first inequality, note that the packet numbered SN_{max} (by definition of SN_{max}) has not entered the DLC unit at node A by time t, and thus can not have started transmission by time t. Since there is a delay of at least T_m+T_d from the time a packet transmission starts until the completion of its reception, packet SN_{max} can not have been received by time $t+T_m+T_d$. Because of the correctness of the protocol, $RN(t+T_m+T_d)$ can be no greater than the number of a packet not yet received, i.e. SN_{max}.

For the second inequality, note that for the transmitter to have a given value of SN_{min} at time t, that value must have been transmitted earlier as the request number in a frame coming back from node B. The latest time that such a frame could have been formed is $t-T_m-T_d$, so by this time RN must have been at least SN_{min}.

2.22

a) If the transmitter never has to go back or wait in the absence of errors, then it can send a continuous stream of new packets in the absence of errors. In order for such a continuous stream to be sent, each packet must be acknowledged (i.e. SN_{min} must advance beyond the packet's number) before the next $n-1$ frames complete transmission. Thus these $n-1$ frame transmission times are in a race with the time, first, for the given packet to propagate over the channel and, second, for the acknowledgement to wait for the feedback frame in progress, then wait to be transmitted in the next feedback frame and propagated back to the original transmitter. In order for the feedback to always win the race, the minimum time for the $n-1$ frames to be transmitted must be greater than the maximum time for the feedback, i.e.,

$$(n-1)T_{min} > 2T_d + 2T_{max}$$

$$T_{max} < [(n-1)/2]T_{min} - T_d$$

b) If an isolated error occurs in the feedback direction, the feedback could be held up for one additional frame, leading to

$$(n-1)T_{min} > 2T_d + 3T_{max}$$

$$T_{max} < [(n-1)/3]T_{min} - (2/3)T_d$$

2.23

After a given packet is transmitted from node A, the second subsequent frame transmission termination from B carries the acknowledgement (recall that the frame transmission in progress from B when A finishes its transmission cannot carry the ack for that transmission; recall also that propagation and processing delays are negligible. Thus q is the probability of n-1 frame terminations from A before the second frame termination from B. This can be rephrased as the probability that out of the next n frame terminations from either node, either n-1 or n come from node A. Since successive frame terminations are equally likely and independently from A or B, this probability is

$$q = \sum_{i=n-1}^{n} \frac{n!}{i!(n-i)!} 2^{-n} = (n+1)2^{-n}$$

2.24

If an isolated error in the feedback direction occurs, then the ack for a given packet is held up by one frame in the feedback direction (i.e., the number RN in the feedback frame following the feedback frame in error reacknowledges the old packet as well as any new packet that might have been received in the interim). Thus q is now the probability of n-1 frame terminations from A before 3 frame terminations from B (one for the frame in progress, one for the frame in error, and one for the frame actually carrying the ack; see the solution to problem 2.23). This is the probability that n-1 or more of the next n+1 frame terminations come from A; since each termination is from A or B independently and with equal probability,

$$q = \sum_{i=n-1}^{n} \left(\frac{(n+1)!}{i!(n+1-i)!} \right) 2^{-n-1} = [n+2+(n+1)n/2]2^{-n-1}$$

2.25

As in the solution to problem 2.23, q is the probability of n-1 frame terminations coming from node A before two frame terminations come from node B. Frame terminations from A (and similarly from B) can be regarded as alternate points in a Poisson point process from A (or from B). There are two cases to consider. In the first, the initial frame is received from A after an even numbered point in the Poisson process at B, and in the second, the initial frame is received after an odd numbered point. In the first case, q is the probability that 2n-2 Poisson events from A occur before 4 Poisson events occur from B. This is the probability, in a combined Poisson point process of Poisson events from A and B, that 2n-2 or more Poisson events come from A out of the next 2n+1 events in the combined process. In the second case, q is the probability that 2n-2 Poisson events from A occur before 3 events occur from B. Since these cases are equally likely,

$$q = \frac{1}{2} \sum_{i=2n-2}^{2n+1} \left(\frac{(2n+1)!}{i!(2n+1-i)!} \right) 2^{-2n-1} + \frac{1}{2} \sum_{i=2n-2}^{2n} \left(\frac{(2n)!}{i!(2n-i)!} \right) 2^{-2n}$$

2.26

We view the system from the receiver and ask for the expected number of frames, γ, arriving at the receiver starting immediately after a frame containing a packet that is accepted and running until the next frame containing a packet that is accepted. By the assumptions of the problem, if the packet in a frame is accepted, then the next frame must contain the next packet in order (if not, the transmitter must have gone back to some earlier packet, which is impossible since that earlier packet was accepted earlier and by assumption was acked in time to avoid the go back).

Since the next frame after a packet acceptance must contain the awaited packet, that packet is accepted with probability 1-p. With probability p, on the other hand, that next frame contains an error. In this case, some number of frames, say j, follow this next frame before the awaited packet is again contained in a frame. This new frame might again contain an error, but the expected number of frames until the awaited packet is accepted, starting with this new frame, is again γ. Thus, given an error in the frame after a packet acceptance, and given j further frames before the awaited packet is repeated, the expected number of frames from one acceptance to the next is $1+j+\gamma$.

Note that j is the number of frames that the transmitter sends, after the above frame in error, up to and including the frame in transmission when feedback arrives concerning the frame in error. Thus the expected value of j is β. Combining the events of error and no error on the next frame after a packet acceptance, we have

$$\gamma = (1-p) + p(1+\beta+\gamma) = 1 + p(\beta+\gamma)$$

Solving for γ and for $v = 1/\gamma$,

$$\gamma = (1+\beta p)/(1-p) \qquad v = (1-p)/(1+\beta p)$$

2.27

Note that the sending DLC could save only one packet if it waited for acknowledgements rather than continuing to transmit. Similarly the sending DLC could save an arbitrarily large number of packets by taking packets from the network layer at a rate faster than they can be transmitted. Thus what is desired is to show that at most $\beta+1$ packets need be stored without ever forcing the transmitter to wait. Thus we assume that a new packet is admitted from the network layer only when there are no previously transmitted packets that are known to have been unsuccessful on the last transmission (i.e. the system repeats nak'ed packets before accepting and transmitting new packets; the system accepts and transmits new packets while waiting for feedback information on old packets).

When the system is first initiated, one packet is admitted to the sending DLC from the network layer. We use this as the basis of an inductive argument on successive times at which a new frame is generated. By the inductive hypothesis, at most $\beta+1$ packets were stored at the end of the previous frame generation instant. At the time of generating the new frame, there are at most β outstanding frames (including the one just being completed) for which feedback has not been received. A new packet will be accepted from the network layer only if all packets stored are also in frames for which no feedback has yet been received. Thus if a new packet is accepted, the total number saved is increased to at most $\beta+1$, and if no new packet is accepted, the total number saved remains (by the inductive hypothesis) no more than $\beta+1$.

2.28

Under the given assumptions, the ARPANET ARQ works like ideal select repeat. That is, frames from the 8 channels can be sent in round robin order and the feedback for a channel is always available by time the channel is to be reused. Thus a packet is repeated if and only if the previous transmission was unsuccessful. Since all channels are constantly busy and only the frames in error lead to retransmission, the efficiency is 1-p.

2.29

a) When packet z is transmitted, the transmitter rule ensures that $z \leq SN_{min}+n-1$. At that time, $SN_{min} \leq RN$ since a packet cannot be acked before being received. Thus, at transmit time

$$z \leq RN + n - 1$$

Since RN is nondecreasing, this is also satisfied at receive time. To derive the lower bound on z, note that the transmitter rule specifies $z \geq SN_{min}$. Since $SN_{min}+n$ has never been sent before the current transmission of z, the first come first serve order on the link ensures that it is not received before z. Thus y_{top} at receive time is less than $SN_{min}+n$ at transmit time, so

$$z \geq SN_{min} > y_{top} - n$$

$$z \geq y_{top} - n + 1$$

b) We must ensure that m is large enough to always satisfy

$$z + m > y_{top} + k$$

We know from a) that $z > y_{top}-n$, and adding n+k to both sides of this equation, we know that $z+n+k > y_{top}+k$. Thus, choosing m = n+k (or, more generally, $m \geq n+k$) always satisfies the above equation. If m is chosen any smaller (say m = n+k-1), then when z = $y_{top}-n+1$ (which can happen after a goback), z+m will equal $y_{top}+k$, causing erroneous operation.

c) From b), $m \geq n+k > n$. From Eq. (2.47), $z \leq RN+n-1 < RN+m$; thus z-m < RN.

d) From b) and c), $m \geq n+k$ assures correct operation at the receiver. Since m > n, correct operation at the transmitter is assured as in goback n.

e) Initially $y_{top} = RN-1$, so for k=1, the receiver can initially accept only RN. On each accepted packet, RN and y_{top} are each incremented by 1, so at all times only RN can be accepted. Thus k=1 is ordinary goback n ARQ. For k=n, all received z must satisfy $z \leq y_{top} +k$, and we have ordinary selective repeat ARQ.

2.30

a) The sequence below shows the stuffed bits underlined for easy readability:

0 1 1 0 1 1 1 1 1 <u>0</u> 0 0 1 1 1 1 1 <u>0</u> 1 0 1 0 1 1 1 1 1 <u>0</u> 1 1 1 1 1 <u>0</u> 0 1 1 1 0 1 0

b) Here the flags are shown underlined and the removed (destuffed) bits as x's:

$\underline{0\,1\,1\,1\,1\,1\,1\,0}\,1\,1\,1\,1\,1\,x\,1\,1\ \ 0\,0\,1\,1\,1\,1\,1\,x\,0\,1\,1\,1\,1\,1\,x\,1\,1\,1\,1\,1\,x\,1\,1$

$0\,0\,\underline{0\,1\,1\,1\,1\,1\,1\,0}\,1\,0\,1\,1\,1\,1\,1\,x$

2.31

The modified destuffing rule starts at the beginning of the string and destuffs bit by bit. A zero is removed from the string if the previous six bits in the already destuffed portion of the string have the value 01^5. For the given example, the destuffed string, with flags shown underlined and removed bits shown as x's, is as follows:

$0\,1\,1\,0\,1\,1\,1\,1\,1\,x\,1\,1\,1\,1\,1\,1\,0\,1\,1\,1\,1\,1\,x\,1\,\underline{0\,1\,1\,1\,1\,1\,1\,0}$

2.32

The hint shows that the data string $01^501x_1x_2$... must have a zero stuffed after 01^5, thus appearing as $01^500x_1x_2$.... This stuffed pattern will be indistinguishable from the original string $01^500x_1x_2$... unless stuffing is also used after 01^5 in the string $01^500x_1x_2$.... Thus stuffing must be used in this case. The general argument is then by induction. Assume that stuffing is necessary after 01^5 on all strings of the form $01^50^kx_1x_2$.... Then such a stuffed sequence is $01^50^{k+1}x_1x_2$.... It follows as before that stuffing is then necessary after 01^5 in the sequence $01^50^{k+1}x_1x_2$.... Thus stuffing is always necessary after 01^5.

2.33

The stuffed string is shown below with the stuffed bits underlined and a flag added at the end.

$1\,1\,0\,1\,1\,0\,1\,0\,\underline{0}\,0\,1\,0\,\underline{0}\,1\,0\,\underline{0}\,1\,1\,1\,0\,1\,0\,\underline{0}\,1\,0\,1$

The destuffing rule is to decode (destuff) the string bit by bit starting at the beginning. A given 0 bit is then deleted from the string if the preceding three decoded bits are 010. The flag is detected when a 1 is preceded by the three decoded bits 010 and the most recently decoded bit was not deleted. The above is a general rule for detecting any type of flag sequence, rather than just 0101; for this special case, it is sufficient to look for the substring 0101 in the received string; the reason for the simplification is that if an insertion occurs within the flag, it has to occur by simply a repetition of the first flag bit.

2.34

Let γ be $\log_2 E\{K\} - j$. Since j is the integer part of $\log_2 E\{K\}$, we see that γ must lie between 0 and 1. Expressing $A = E\{K\}2^{-j} + j + 1$ in terms of γ and $E\{K\}$, we get

$$A = 2^\gamma + \log_2 E\{K\} - \gamma + 1$$

$$A - \log_2 E\{K\} = 2^\gamma - \gamma + 1$$

This function of γ is easily seen to be convex (i.e., it has a positive second derivative). It has the value 2 at $\gamma = 0$ and at $\gamma = 1$ and is less than 2 for $0 < \gamma < 1$. This establishes that

$$A \leq \log_2 E\{K\} + 2$$

Finding the minimum of $2^\gamma - \gamma + 1$ by differentiation, the minimum occurs at

$$\gamma = -\log_2(\ln 2)$$

The value of $2^\gamma - \gamma + 1$ at this minimizing point is $[\ln 2]^{-1} + \log_2(\ln 2) + 1 = 1.914...$, so

$$A \geq \log_2 E\{K\} + (\ln 2)^{-1} + \log_2(\ln 2) + 1$$

2.35

Stuffed bits are always 0's and always follow the pattern 01^5. The initial 0 in this pattern could be a bit in the unstuffed data string, or could itself be a stuffed bit. As in the analysis of subsection 2.5.2, we ignore the case where this initial 0 is a stuffed bit since it is almost negligible compared with the other case (also a well designed flag detector would not allow a stuffed bit as the first bit of a flag). If a stuffed bit (preceded by 01^5 in the data) is converted by noise into a 1, then it is taken as a flag if the next bit is 0 and is taken as an abort if the next bit is 1. Thus an error in a stuffed bit causes a flag to appear with probability 1/2 and the expected number of falsely detected flags due to errors in stuffed bits is $K2^{-7}$. If one is less crude in the approximations, one sees that there are only K-6 places in the data stream where a stuffed bit could be inserted following 01^5 in the data; thus a more refined answer is that the expected number of falsely detected flags due to errors in stuffed bits is $(K-6)2^{-7}$.

There are eight patterns of eight bits such that an error in one of the eight bits would turn the pattern into a flag. Two of these patterns, 01^7 and 1^70, cannot appear in stuffed data. Another two of the patterns, 01^500 and 001^50, can appear in stuffed data but must contain a stuffed bit (i.e. the 0 following 1^5). The first of these cases corresponds to the case in which an error in a stuffed bit causes a flag to appear, and we have already analyzed this. The second corresponds to a data string 001^5. Thus the substrings of data for which a single error in a data bit can cause a flag to appear are listed below; the position in which the error must appear is shown underlined:

```
0 0 1 1 1 1 1
0 1 0 1 1 1 1 0
0 1 1 0 1 1 1 0
0 1 1 1 0 1 1 0
0 1 1 1 1 0 1 0
```

For any given bit position j in the K bit data string $(j \leq K-7)$, the probability that one of these patterns starts on bit j is $2^{-7} + 4.2^{-8} = 3.2^{-7}$. Thus the probability of a false flag being detected because of an error on a data bit, starting on bit j of the data is $3p2^{-7}$. This is also the expected number of such flags, and summing over the bits of the data stream, the expected number is $(K-7)3p2^{-7}$. Approximating by replacing K-7 by K, and adding this to the expected number of false flags due to errors in stuffed bits, the overall probability of a false flag in a frame of length K is $(1/32)Kp$. If K-7 is not approximated by K, and if we recognize that the first pattern above can also appear starting at j=K-6, then the overall probability of a false flag is approximated more closely by $(1/32)(K-6.5)p$.

2.36

Let N be the number of overhead bits per packet, F the number of flag bits per packet, U the number of unary code bits per packet, and I the number of insertions per packet. Then

$$N = F + U + I; \qquad E\{N\} = E\{F\} + E\{U\} + E\{I\}$$

A flag will occur at the end of a packet if the next session has nothing to send; thus a flag (containing K bits) occurs at the end of a packet with probability p. It follows that

$$E\{F\} = pK$$

The number of unary bits following a packet is 0 if the next session has something to send and is $j \geq 1$ if the number of following sessions with nothing to send is j. Thus $P\{U=j\} = (1-p)p^j$ for $j \geq 1$.

$$E\{U\} = \sum_{j=1}^{\infty} j(1-p)p^j = \frac{p}{1-p}$$

Finally an insertion occurs if a packet starts with 01^{k-2}. Assuming independent equally likely binary digits in the packets (this is not particularly realistic for packet headers, but it is the only reasonable assumption without looking at the details of some particular protocol), the probability of an insertion at the beginning of a packet is $2^{-(K-1)}$. Thus

$$E\{I\} = 2^{-(K-1)}$$

$$E\{N\} = pK + p/(1-p) + 2^{-(K-1)}$$

Note that it is not really necessary to do insertions at the beginning of the first packet following a flag; if one assumes that such insertions are not made, $E\{I\}$ changes to $(1-p)2^{-(K-1)}$.

b) No problems occur using flags both for addressing as above and for DLC. The DLC regards the addressing flags as part of the data (which can be arbitrary anyway), and the stuffing due to the DLC flags is removed before the network layer sees it. This is one of the advantages of layering, that one doesn't have to worry about such interactions. Note however that the use of this particular flag for addressing will cause a slight increase in the number of insertions required at the DLC layer. When efficiency is important, one can not necessarily ignore the interactions between different layers.

2.37

a) Note that a given packet n can never be sent until after n-1 is acked; this is true even without the possibility of packets getting out of order on the line. To see this, consider the example below.

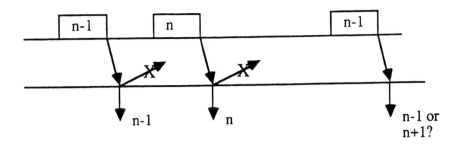

Note also that there is no possible reason to want to send a packet after it has been acked. Thus the only question here is whether it is possible, or sensible, to retransmit a given packet without waiting for an ack or a period 2T . The simplest rule for the transmitter (and probably the most practical unless T is very large) is for the transmitter to wait after sending each packet for either an ack or nak (i.e. RN equal to the sequence number just transmitted) or for a period of 2T, which guarantees that nothing remains on the link.

In order to leave the transmitter with more freedom than the above, we observe that there are three restrictions on when a given packet n can be transmitted. The first, that n-1 must be acknowledged, was mentioned above. The second is that no transmission of packet n-1 can be on the forward channel. The third is that no ack of packet n-2 can be on the return channel. The reason for the second restriction is that a transmission of packet n could arrive before that of n-1, causing n-1 to be mistaken for n+1. The reason for the third restriction is to avoid the ack for n-2 being mistaken for the ack for n. Letting t_1 be the time at which n-1 was last transmitted, we see that the second restriction above leads to the following rule. In order to transmit packet n at time t, one or more of the following conditions must be satisfied:

    i) $t \geq t_1 + T$

    ii) The number of acks of n-1 equals the number of transmissions of n-1 up to t

    iii) The last ack of n-1 is over 2T seconds after the next to last transmission of n-1.

In addition, from restriction 2, one or more of the following conditions must also be satisfied, where t_2 is the time at which n-2 was last transmitted:

    i) $t \geq t_2 + 2T$

    ii) The number of acks of n-2 equals the number of transmissions of n-2

    iii) The last ack of n-2 is over 2T seconds after the next to last transmission of n-2.

b) An algorithm must deal with the possibility of a frame that is lost (i.e., never arrives), and must successfully transmit packets after a frame is lost. If an algorithm succeeds in this case, then it must fail if a frame, regarded as lost, later arrives when a new packet of the same sequence number modulo 2 is expected.

2.38

For simplicity, look first at the case in which A and B both start at the same time.

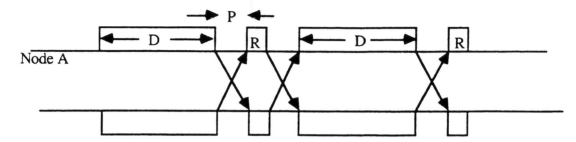

It can be seen that the above pattern is periodic with period D+R+2P, with one packet in each direction per period. Thus the rate is $(D+R+2P)^{-1}$.

Next, without loss of generality, suppose B starts its first transmission after A:

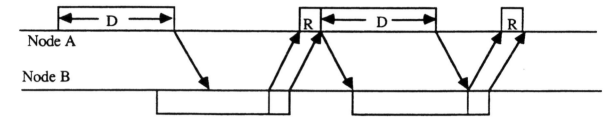

In the figure above, the pattern is periodic after the first frame in each direction. In general, if B completes its first transmission at time t and A completes its first transmission at $\tau \leq t$, then B starts its first ACK transmission at max(t, τ+P), since τ+P is the time at which B has completely received the first packet from A and t is the first time that the link is free from A to B. Node A starts to send its first ACK to B at t+P, which is thus received at B at t+R+2P. Similarly, node A receives the first ACK from B at max(t, τ+P)+R+P, at which time it starts to send its second packet.

b) The diagram below makes it clear that the two way transmission pattern is periodic with a period of 2D+2D, leading to rate $(2D+2P)^{-1}$.

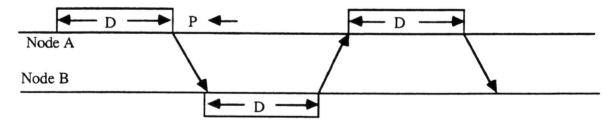

2.39

a) $TC = (K+V)(j-1) + (K+V)\lceil M/K \rceil$

b) $E\{TC\} \approx (K+V)[j-1+(M/K)+1/2]$

Differentiating with respect to K and setting the result equal to 0, we get

$$K = \sqrt{\frac{MV}{j-1/2}}$$

c) For j=1, it can be seen directly from Eq. (2.42) that TC is minimized by choosing K_{MAX} greater than the largest possible value of M (thus making all messages one packet long). The approximation in Eq. (2.43) is very poor in this case, but the solution $K_{MAX}=\infty$ in Eq. (2.44) is still valid, as seen above. For fixed length packets, the amount of fill required for very large K is prohibitive, so the approximation used in part b) above is reasonable and the resulting finite value for K is certainly reasonable.

2.40

a) Using the properties of the A->B master slave protocol, B eventually receives the DISC message from A (perhaps after many attempts, using the assumption that each frame is correctly received with some probability bounded away from 0). Node B, if it has not already started to disconnect, will start to send DISC, which by the same argument is eventually received by A. Similarly B sends ACKD, which is eventually received by A (perhaps after many receptions of DISC at B and retransmissions of ACKD to A), and A regards the link as down after receiving both DISC and ACKD. Finally, when A receives DISC, it sends ACKD, which is eventually received by B, perhaps after many retransmissions of DISC from B and ACKD from A.

b) In the argument above, A regards the link as down upon receiving both DISC and ACKD, but there is no need for B to have received ACKD by this time. Thus A can start to re-initialize the link before B receives ACKD, and thus before B regards the link as down.

c) Note that the case being investigated here is symmetric (interchanging initialize and disconnect) to the example in part b, and thus the demonstration here shows that the example there causes no problems. Node B continues to send INIT (according to the B->A master/slave protocol) until receiving ACKI. Node A responds to each of these messages, but also sends a piggybacked ACKI when it attempts to disconnect by sending DISC. Thus node B must receive ACKI before or simultaneously with receiving DISC; in the simultaneous case, B regards the link as up instantaneously before starting to disconnect, and from this point, the scenario is the same as in part a). Note that the piggybacking is essential here, although alternate ways exist of co-ordinating the two master/slave protocols.

2.41

a)

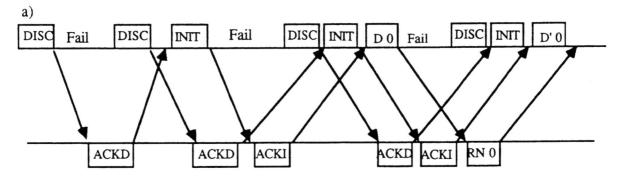

b)

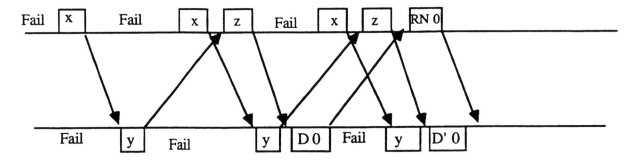

2.42

The protocol requires each node to respond to each INIT or DISC message with an ACKI or ACKD message. Thus if an additional INIT or DISC message were sent with each such ack, the protocol would continue to bounce messages back and forth forever, whereas there should be no need to continue to send INIT messages during up periods or DISC messages during down periods.

2.43

Consider integer numbering rather than numbering modulo m. Suppose packet number SN is sent at time t_1 and received at t_2. Let $SN_{min}(t_1)$ be the lower edge of the window at t_1 and $RN(t_2)$ be the lowest numbered packet not received by t_2. Because of the window, we have

$$SN_{min}(t_1) \leq SN \leq SN_{min}(t_1) + n - 1$$

Since $SN_{min}(t_1)$ is the greatest value of RN received up to t_1, and since $RN(t)$ is increasing with t at node B,

$$SN_{min}(t_1) \leq RN(t_2)$$

Combining these equations, $SN \leq RN(t_2) + n - 1$. Conversely, at most M packets can be sent after packet number SN and before SN arrives at node B. Also, the packets on the link or already received at t_1 have numbers at most $SN_{min}(t_1)+n-1$. Thus the highest consecutive numbered packet received by time t_2 must be at most $SN_{min}(t_1)+n+M-1$, and $RN(t_2) \leq SN_{min}(t_1)+n+M$. Combining these relationships,

$$RN(t_2) - n - M \leq SN \leq RN(t_2) + n - 1$$

Thus the range of possible values of SN that could be received at t_2, including the end points, is $2n+M$, and the modulus m must be that large to enable the sequence numbers to be properly interpreted at the receiver.

Next suppose a receive number $RN = RN(t_1)$ is sent at t_1 from B and is received at t_2 at node A. The largest possible value of $SN_{min}(t_2)$ occurs if node B receives packet RN at t_1^+ and has already received $RN+1,...RN+n-1$. Node B then sends $RN+n$ as a receive number, which can be received by A by t_1^+. Node A then sends $RN+n, ...RN+n+M-1$ before t_2, and node B can send at most $RN+n+M$ before t_2. Thus, $SN_{min}(t_2) \leq RN+n+M$. It follows that $SN_{max}(t_2) \leq RN+2n+M-1$. Thus, $m \geq 2n+M$ guarantees that RN, arriving at t_2, will not be falsely interpreted as a request for $SN_{max}(t_2)$.

CHAPTER 3 SOLUTIONS

3.1

A customer that carries out the order (eats in the restaurant) stays for 5 mins (25 mins). Therefore the average customer time in the system is $T = 0.5*5 + 0.5*25 = 15$. By Little's Theorem the average number in the system is $N = \lambda*T = 5*15 = 75$.

3.2

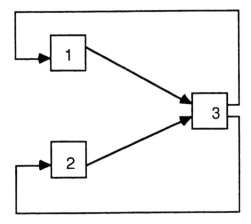

We represent the system as shown in the figure. The number of files in the entire system is exactly one at all times. The average number in node i is $\lambda_i R_i$ and the average number in node 3 is $\lambda_1 P_1 + \lambda_2 P_2$. Therefore the throughput pairs (λ_1, λ_2) must satisfy (in addition to nonnegativity) the constraint

$$\lambda_1(R_1 + P_1) + \lambda_2(R_2 + P_2) = 1.$$

If the system were slightly different and queueing were allowed at node 3, while nodes 1 and 2 could transmit at will, a different analysis would apply. The transmission bottleneck for the files of node 1 implies that

$$\lambda_1 \leq \frac{1}{R_1}$$

Similarly for node 2 we get that

$$\lambda_2 \leq \frac{1}{R_2}$$

Node 3 can work on only one file at a time. If we look at the file receiving service at node 3 as a system and let N be the average number receiving service at node 3, we conclude from Little's theorem that

$$\lambda_1 P_1 + \lambda_2 P_2 = N$$

and $N \leq 1$

This implies that

$$\lambda_1 P_1 + \lambda_2 P_2 \leq 1$$

3.3

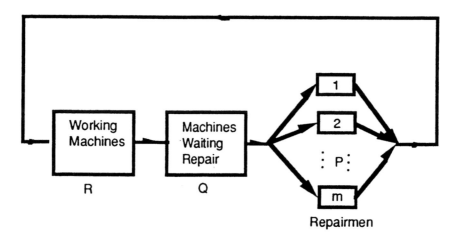

We represent the system as shown in the figure. In particular, once a machine breaks down, it goes into repair if a repairperson is available at the time, and otherwise waits in a queue for a repairperson to become free. Note that if m=1 this system is identical to the one of Example 3.7.

Let λ be the throughput of the system and let Q be the average time a broken down machine waits for a repairperson to become free. Applying Little's theorem to the entire system, we obtain

$$\lambda(R+Q+P) = N \tag{1}$$

from which

$$\lambda(R+P) \leq N \tag{2}$$

Since the number of machines waiting repair can be at most (N-m), the average waiting time λQ is at most the average time to repair (N-m) machines, which is (N-m)P. Thus, from Eq. (1) we obtain

$$\lambda(R+ (N - m)P + P) \geq N \tag{3}$$

Applying Little's theorem to the repairpersons, we obtain

$$\lambda P \leq m \tag{4}$$

The relations (2)-(4) give the following bounds for the throughput λ

$$\frac{N}{R + (N - m + 1)P} \leq \lambda \leq \min\left\{\frac{m}{P}, \frac{N}{R + P}\right\} \tag{5}$$

Note that these bounds generalize the ones obtained n Example 3.7 (see Eq. (3.9)).
By using the equation $T = N/\lambda$ for the average time between repairs, we obtain from Eq. (5)

$$\min\{NP/m, R + P\} \leq T \leq R + (N - m + 1)P$$

3.4

If λ is the throughput of the system, Little's theorem gives $N = \lambda T$, so from the relation $T = \alpha + \beta N^2$ we obtain $T = \alpha + \beta \lambda^2 T^2$ or

$$\lambda = \sqrt{\frac{T - \alpha}{\beta T^2}} \tag{1}$$

This relation betweeen λ ands T is plotted below.

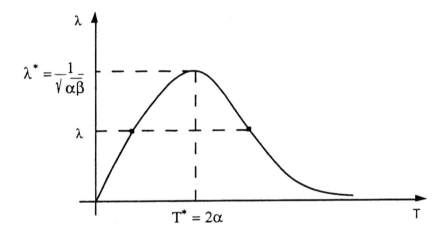

The maximum value of λ is attained for the value T^* for which the derivative of $(T - \alpha)/\beta T^2$ is zero (or $1/(\beta T^2) - 2(T - \alpha)/(\beta T^3) = 0$). This yields $T^* = 2\alpha$ and from Eq. (1), the corresponding maximal throughput value

$$\lambda^* = \frac{1}{\sqrt{\alpha\beta}} \tag{2}$$

(b) When $\lambda < \lambda^*$, there are two corresponding values of T: a low value corresponding to an uncongested system where N is relatively low, and a high value corresponding to a congested system where N is relatively high. This assumes that the system reaches a steady-state. However, it can be argued that when the system is congested a small increase in the number of cars in the system due to statistical fluctuations will cause an increase in the time in the system, which will tend to decrease the rate of departure of cars from the system. This will cause a further increase in the number in the system and a further increase in the time in the system, etc. In other words, when we are operating on the right side of the curve of the figure, there is a tendency for *instability* in the system, whereby a steady-state is never reached: the system tends to drift towards a traffic jam where the car departure rate from the system tends towards zero and the time a car spends in the system tends towards infinity. Phenomena of this type are analyzed in the context of the Aloha multiaccess system in Chapter 4.

3.5

The expected time in question equals

$$E\{Time\} = (5 + E\{stay\ of\ 2nd\ student\})*P\{1st\ stays\ less\ or\ equal\ to\ 5\ minutes\}$$
$$+ (E\{stay\ of\ 1st\ |\ stay\ of\ 1st \geq 5\} + E\{stay\ of\ 2nd\})*$$
$$P\{1st\ stays\ more\ than\ 5\ minutes\}.$$

We have $E\{stay\ of\ 2nd\ student\} = 30$, and, using the memoryless property of the exponential distribution,

$$E\{stay\ of\ 1st\ |\ stay\ of\ 1st \geq 5\} = 5 + E\{stay\ of\ 1st\} = 35.$$

Also

$$P\{1st\ student\ stays\ less\ or\ equal\ to\ 5\ minutes\} = 1 - e^{-5/30}$$
$$P\{1st\ student\ stays\ more\ than\ 5\ minutes\} = e^{-5/30}.$$

By substitution we obtain

$$E\{Time\} = (5 + 30)*(1 - e^{-5/30}) + (35 + 30)* e^{-5/30} = 35 + 30*e^{-5/30} = 60.394.$$

3.6

(a) The probability that the person will be the last to leave is 1/4 because the exponential distribution is memoryless, and all customers have identical service time distribution. In particular, at the instant the customer enters service, the remaining service time of each of the other three customers served has the same distribution as the service time of the customer.

(b) The average time in the bank is 1 (the average customer service time) plus the expected time for the first customer to finish service. The latter time is 1/4 since the departure process is statistically identical to that of a single server facility with 4 times larger service rate. More precisely we have

$$P\{no\ customer\ departs\ in\ the\ next\ t\ mins\} = P\{1st\ does\ not\ depart\ in\ next\ t\ mins\}$$
$$* P\{2nd\ does\ not\ depart\ in\ next\ t\ mins\}$$
$$* P\{3rd\ does\ not\ depart\ in\ next\ t\ mins\}$$
$$* P\{4th\ does\ not\ depart\ in\ next\ t\ mins\}$$
$$= (e^{-t})^4 = e^{-4t}.$$

Therefore

$$P\{the\ first\ departure\ occurs\ within\ the\ next\ t\ mins\} = 1 - e^{-4t},$$

and the expected time to the next depature is 1/4. So the answer is 5/4 minutes.

(c) The answer will not change because the situation at the instant when the customer begins service will be the same under the conditions for (a) and the conditions for (c).

3.7

In the statistical multiplexing case the packets of at most one of the streams will wait upon arrival for a packet of the other stream to finish transmission. Let W be the waiting time , and note that $0 \leq W \leq T/2$. We have that one half of the packets have system time $T/2 + W$ and waiting time in queue W. Therefore

Average System Time $= (1/2)T/2 + (1/2)(T/2+W) = (T+W)/2$
Average Waiting Time in Queue $= W/2$
Variance of Waiting Time $= (1/2)(W/2)^2 + (1/2)(W/2)^2 = W^2/4.$

So the average system time is between $T/2$ and $3T/4$ and the variance of waiting time is between 0 and $T^2/16$.

3.8

Packet Arrivals

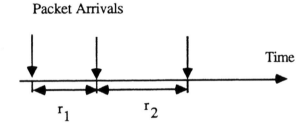

Fix a packet. Let r_1 and r_2 be the interarrival times between a packet and its immediate predecessor, and successor respectively as shown in the figure above. Let X_1 and X_2 be the lengths of the predecessor packet, and of the packet itself respectively. We have:

$$P\{\text{No collision w/ predecessor or successor}\} = P\{r_1 > X_1, r_2 > X_2\}$$
$$= P\{r_1 > X_1\}P\{r_2 > X_2\}.$$

$$P\{\text{No collision with any other packet}\} = P_1 P\{r_2 > X_2\}$$

where

$$P_1 = P\{\text{No collision with all preceding packets}\}.$$

(a) For fixed packet lengths (= 20 msec)

$$P\{r_1 > X_1\} = P\{r_2 > X_2\} = e^{-\lambda*20} = e^{-0.01*20} = e^{-0.2}$$
$$P_1 = P\{r_1 \leq X_1\}.$$

Therefore the two probabilities of collision are both equal to $e^{-0.4} = 0.67$.

(b) For X exponentially distributed packet length with mean $1/\mu$ we have

$$P\{r_1 > X_1\} = P\{r_2 > X_2\} = \int_0^\infty P\{r_1 > X \mid X_1 = X\}p\{X_1 = X\}dX$$

$$= \int_0^\infty e^{-\lambda X}\mu e^{-\mu X}dX = \frac{\mu}{\lambda + \mu}$$

Substituting $\lambda = 0.01$ and $\mu = 0.05$ we obtain $P\{r_1 > X_1\} = P\{r_2 > X_2\} = 5/6$, and

$$P\{\text{No collision w/ predecessor or successor}\} = (5/6)^2 = 0.694.$$

Also P_1 is seen to be the steady-state probability of a customer finding an empty system in the M/M/∞ system with arrival and service rate λ and μ respectively. Therefore $P_1 = e^{-\lambda/\mu} = e^{-0.2}$. Therefore

$$P\{\text{No collision with any other packet}\} = e^{-0.2}5/6 = 0.682.$$

3.9

(a) For each session the arrival rate is $\lambda = 150/60 = 2.5$ packets/sec. When the line is divided into 10 lines of capacity 5 Kbits/sec, the average packet transmission time is $1/\mu = 0.2$ secs. The corresponding utilization factor is $\rho = \lambda/\mu = 0.5$. We have for each session $N_Q = \rho^2/(1 - \rho) = 0.5$, $N = \rho/(1 - \rho) = 1$, and $T = N/\lambda = 0.4$ secs. For all sessions collectively N_Q and N must be multiplied by 10 to give $N_Q = 5$ and $N = 10$.

When statistical multiplexing is used, all sessions are merged into a single session with 10 times larger λ and μ; $\lambda = 25$, $1/\mu = 0.02$. We obtain $\rho = 0.5$, $N_Q = 0.5$, $N = 1$, and $T = 0.04$ secs. Therefore N_Q, N, and T have been reduced by a factor of 10 over the TDM case.

(b) For the sessions transmitting at 250 packets/min we have $\rho = (250/60)*0.2 = 0.833$ and we have $N_Q = (0.833)^2/(1 - 0.833) = 4.158$, $N = 5$, $T = N/\lambda = 5/(250/60) = 1.197$ secs. For the sessions transmitting at 50 packets/min we have $\rho = (50/60)*0.2 = 0.166$, $N_Q = 0.033$, $N = 0.199$, $T = 0.199/(50/60) = 0.239$.

The corresponding averages over all sessions are $N_Q = 5*(4.158 + 0.033) = 21$, $N = 5*(5 +0.199) = 26$, $T = N/\lambda = N/(5*\lambda_1 + 5*\lambda_2) = 26/(5*(250/60)+5*(50/60)) = 1.038$ secs.

When statistical multiplexing is used the arrival rate of the combined session is $5*(250 + 50) = 1500$ packets/sec and the same values for N_Q, N, and T as in (a) are obtained.

3.10

(a) Let t_n be the time of the nth arrival, and $\tau_n = t_{n+1} - t_n$. We have for $s \geq 0$

$$P\{\tau_n > s\} = P\{A(t_n + s) - A(t_n) = 0\} = e^{-\lambda s}$$

(by the Poisson distribution of arrivals in an interval). So

$$P\{\tau_n \leq s\} = 1 - e^{-\lambda s}$$

which is (3.11).

To show that $\tau_1, \tau_2, \ldots$ are independent, note that (using the independence of the numbers of arrivals in disjoint intervals)

$$P\{\tau_2 > s \mid \tau_1 = \tau\} = P\{0 \text{ arrivals in } (\tau, \tau+s] \mid \tau_1 = \tau\}$$
$$= P\{0 \text{ arrivals in } (\tau, \tau+s]\} = e^{-\lambda s} = P\{\tau_2 > s\}$$

Therefore τ_2 and τ_1 are independent.

To verify (3.12), we observe that

$$P\{A(t + \delta) - A(t) = 0\} = e^{-\lambda \delta}$$

so (3.12) will be shown if

$$\lim_{\delta \to 0} (e^{-\lambda \delta} - 1 + \lambda \delta)/\delta = 0$$

Indeed, using L'Hospital's rule we have

$$\lim_{\delta \to 0} (e^{-\lambda \delta} - 1 + \lambda \delta)/\delta = \lim_{\delta \to 0} (-\lambda e^{-\lambda \delta} + \lambda) = 0$$

To verify (3.13) we note that

$$P\{A(t + \delta) - A(t) = 1\} = \lambda \delta e^{-\lambda \delta}$$

so (3.13) will be shown if

$$\lim_{\delta \to 0} (\lambda \delta e^{-\lambda \delta} - \lambda \delta)/\delta = 0$$

This is equivalent to

$$\lim_{\delta \to 0} (\lambda e^{-\lambda \delta} - \lambda) = 0$$

which is clearly true.

To verify (3.14) we note that

$$P\{A(t + \delta) - A(t) \geq 2\} = 1 - P\{A(t + \delta) - A(t) = 0\} - P\{A(t + \delta) - A(t) = 1\}$$

$$= 1 - (1 - \lambda\delta + o(\delta)) - (\lambda\delta + o(\delta)) = o(\delta)$$

(b) Let N_1, N_2 be the number of arrivals in two disjoint intervals of lengths τ_1 and τ_2. Then

$$
\begin{aligned}
P\{N_1+N_2 = n\} &= \Sigma^n_{k=0}P\{N_1 = k, N_2 = n-k\} = \Sigma^n_{k=0}P\{N_1 = k\}P\{N_2 = n-k\} \\
&= \Sigma^n_{k=0}e^{-\lambda\tau 1}[(\lambda\tau_1)^k/k!]e^{-\lambda\tau 2}[(\lambda\tau_2)^{(n-k)}/(n-k)!] \\
&= e^{-\lambda(\tau 1 + \tau 2)}\Sigma^n_{k=0}[(\lambda\tau_1)^k(\lambda\tau_2)^{(n-k)}]/[k!(n-k)!] \\
&= e^{-\lambda(\tau 1 + \tau 2)}[(\lambda\tau_1 + \lambda\tau_2)^n/n!]
\end{aligned}
$$

(The identity

$$\Sigma^n_{k=0}[a^k b^{(n-k)}]/[k!(n-k)!] = (a + b)^n/n!$$

can be shown by induction.)

(c) The number of arrivals of the combined process in disjoint intervals is clearly independent, so we need to show that the number of arrivals in an interval is Poisson distributed, i.e.

$$
\begin{aligned}
P\{A_1(t + \tau) + \ldots + A_k(t + \tau) - A_1(t) - \ldots - A_k(t) = n\} \\
= e^{-(\lambda 1 + \ldots + \lambda k)\tau}[(\lambda_1 + \ldots + \lambda_k)\tau]^n/n!
\end{aligned}
$$

For simplicity let k=2; a similar proof applies for k > 2. Then

$$
\begin{aligned}
P\{A_1(t + \tau) + A_2(t + \tau) - A_1(t) - A_2(t) = n\} \\
= \Sigma^n_{m=0}P\{A_1(t + \tau) - A_1(t) = m, A_2(t + \tau) - A_2(t) = n-m\} \\
= \Sigma^n_{m=0}P\{A_1(t + \tau) - A_1(t) = m\}P\{A_2(t + \tau) - A_2(t) = n-m\}
\end{aligned}
$$

and the calculation continues as in part (b). Also

$$
\begin{aligned}
P\{1 \text{ arrival from } A_1 \text{ prior to } t \mid 1 \text{ occured}\} \\
= P\{1 \text{ arrival from } A_1, 0 \text{ from } A_2\}/P\{1 \text{ occured}\} \\
= (\lambda_1 te^{-\lambda 1 t}e^{-\lambda 2 t})/(\lambda te^{-\lambda t}) = \lambda_1/\lambda
\end{aligned}
$$

(d) Let t be the time of arrival. We have

$$
\begin{aligned}
P\{t < s \mid 1 \text{ arrival occured}\} &= P\{t < s, 1 \text{ arrival occured}\}/P\{1 \text{ arrival occured}\} \\
&= P\{1 \text{ arrival occured in } [t_1, s), 0 \text{ arrivals occured in } [s, t_2]\}/P\{1 \text{ arrival occured}\} \\
&= (\lambda(s - t_1)e^{-\lambda(s - t 1)}e^{-\lambda(s - t 2)})/(\lambda(t_2 - t_1)e^{-\lambda(t 2 - t 1)}) = (s - t_1)/(t_2 - t_1)
\end{aligned}
$$

This shows that the arrival time t is uniformly distributed in $[t_1, t_2]$.

3.11

(a) Let us call the two transmission lines 1 and 2, and let $N_1(t)$ and $N_2(t)$ denote the respective numbers of packet arrivals in the interval [0,t]. Let also $N(t) = N_1(t) + N_2(t)$. We calculate the joint probability $P\{N_1(t) = n, N_2(t) = m\}$. To do this we first condition on $N(t)$ to obtain

$$P\{N_1(t) = n, N_2(t) = m\} = \Sigma_{\kappa=0}^{\infty} P\{N_1(t) = n, N_2(t) = m \mid N(t) = k\}P\{N(t) = k\}.$$

Since

$$P\{N_1(t) = n, N_2(t) = m \mid N(t) = k\} = 0 \qquad \text{when} \quad k \neq n+m$$

we obtain

$$
\begin{aligned}
P\{N_1(t) = n, N_2(t) = m\} &= P\{N_1(t) = n, N_2(t) = m \mid N(t) = n + m\}P\{N(t) = n + m\} \\
&= P\{N_1(t) = n, N_2(t) = m \mid N(t) = n + m\}e^{-\lambda t}[(\lambda t)^{n+m}/(n + m)!]
\end{aligned}
$$

However, given that n+m arrivals occurred, since each arrival has probability p of being a line 1 arrival and probability 1-p of being a line 2 arrival, it follows that the probability that n of them will be line 1 and m of them will be line 2 arrivals is the binomial probability

$$\binom{n+m}{n}p^n(1 - p)^m$$

Thus

$$P\{N_1(t) = n, N_2(t) = m\} = \binom{n+m}{n}p^n(1 - p)^m e^{-\lambda t}\frac{(\lambda t)^{n+m}}{(n+m)!}$$

$$= e^{-\lambda t p}\frac{(\lambda t p)^n}{n!} \; e^{-\lambda t(1-p)}\frac{(\lambda t(1-p))^m}{m!} \qquad (1)$$

Hence

$$P\{N_1(t) = n\} = \sum_{m=0}^{\infty} P\{N_1(t) = n, N_2(t) = m\}$$

$$= e^{-\lambda t p}\frac{(\lambda t p)^n}{(n)!} \sum_{m=0}^{\infty} e^{-\lambda t(1-p)}\frac{(\lambda t(1-p))^m}{m!}$$

$$= e^{-\lambda t p}\frac{(\lambda t p)^n}{(n)!}$$

That is, $\{N_1(t), t \geq 0\}$ is a Poisson process having rate λp. Similarly we argue that $\{N_2(t), t \geq 0\}$ is a Poisson process having rate $\lambda(1 - p)$. Finally from Eq. (1) it follows that the two processes are independent since the joint distribution factors into the marginal distributions.

(b) Let A, A_1, and A_2 be as in the hint. Let I be an interarrival interval of A_2 and consider the number of arrivals of A_1 that lie in I. The probability that this number is n is the probability of n successive arrivals of A_1 followed by an arrival of A_2, which is $\rho^n(1 - \rho)$. This is also the probability that a customer finds upon arrival n other customers waiting in an M/M/1 queue. The service time of each of these customers is exponentially distributed with parameter μ, just like the interarrival times of process A. Therefore the waiting time of the customer in the M/M/1 system has the same distribution as the interarrival time of process A_2. Since by part (a), the process A_2 is Poisson with rate $\mu - \lambda$, it follows that the waiting time of the customer in the M/M/1 system is exponentially distributed with parameter $\mu - \lambda$.

3.12

For any scalar s we have using also the independence of τ_1 and τ_2

$$P(\min\{\tau_1, \tau_2\} \geq s) = P(\tau_1 \geq s, \tau_2 \geq s) = P(\tau_1 \geq s) P(\tau_2 \geq s)$$

$$= e^{-\lambda_1 s} e^{-\lambda_2 s} = e^{-(\lambda_1 + \lambda_2)s}$$

Therefore the distribution of $\min\{\tau_1, \tau_2\}$ is exponential with mean $1/(\lambda_1 + \lambda_2)$.

By viewing τ_1 and τ_2 as the arrival times of the first arrivals from two independent Poisson processes fwith rates λ_1 and λ_2, we see that the equation $P(\tau_1 < \tau_2) = \lambda_1/(\lambda_1 + \lambda_2)$ follows from Problem 3.10(c).

Consider the M/M/1 queue and the amount of time spent in a state k>0 between transition into the state and transition out of the state. This time is $\min\{\tau_1, \tau_2\}$, where τ_1 is the time between entry to the state k and the next customer arrival and τ_2 is the time between entry to the state k and the next service completion. Because of the memoryless property of the exponential distribution, τ_1 and τ_2 are exponentially distributed with means $1/\lambda$ and $1/\mu$, respectively. It follows using the fact shown above that the time between entry and exit from stae k is exponentially distributed with mean $1/(\lambda+\mu)$. The probability that the transition will be from k to k+1 is $\lambda/(\lambda+\mu)$ and that the transition will be from k to k-1 is $\mu/(\lambda+\mu)$. For state 0 the amount of time spent is exponentially distributed with mean $1/\lambda$ and the probability of a transition to state 1 is 1. Because of this it can be seen that M/M/1 queue can be described as a continuous Markov chain with the given properties.

3.13

(a) Consider a Markov chain with state

n = Number of people waiting + number of empty taxi positions

Then the state goes from n to n+1 each time a person arrives and goes from n to n-1 (if $n \geq 1$) when a taxi arrives. Thus the system behaves like an M/M/1 queue with arrival rate 1 per min and departure rate 2 per min. Therefore the occupancy distribution is

$$p_n = (1-\rho)/\rho^n$$

where $\rho = 1/2$. State n, for $0 \le n \le 4$ corresponds to 5, 4, 3, 2, 1 taxis waiting while $n > 4$ corresponds to no taxi waiting. Therefore

P{5 taxis waiting} = 1/2
P{4 taxis waiting} = 1/4
P{3 taxis waiting} = 1/8
P{2 taxis waiting} = 1/16
P{1 taxi waiting} = 1/32

and P{no taxi waiting} is obtained by subtracting the sum of the probabilities above from unity. This gives P{no taxi waiting} = 1/32.

(b) See the hint.

(c) This system corresponds to taxis arriving periodically instead of arriving according to a Poisson process. It is the slotted M/D/1 system analyzed in Section 6.3.

3.14

(a) The average message transmission time is $1/\mu = L/C$ so the service rate is $\mu = C/L$. When the number of packets in the system is larger than K, the arrival rate is λ_1. We must have

$$0 \le \lambda_1 < \mu$$
$$0 \le \lambda_2$$

in order for the arrival rate at node A to be less than the service rate for large state values. For these values, therefore, the average number of packets in the system will stay bounded.

(b) The corresponding Markov chain is as shown in the figure below. The steady-state probabilities satisfy

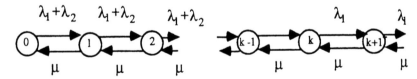

$$p_n = \rho^n p_0 \qquad \text{for } n \le k$$
$$p_n = \rho_1^{n-k}\rho^k p_0 \qquad \text{for } n > k$$

where $\rho = (\lambda_1 + \lambda_2)/\mu$, $\rho_1 = \lambda_1/\mu$. We have

$$\Sigma^\infty_{n=0} p_n = 1$$

or

$$p_0 \Sigma^k_{n=0}\rho^n + \Sigma^\infty_{n=k+1}\rho_1^{n-k}\rho^k = 1$$

from which we obtain after some calculation

$$p_0 = [(1 - \rho)(1 - \rho_1)]/[1 - \rho_1 - \rho^k(\rho - \rho_1)] \qquad \text{for } \rho < 1$$

and

$$p_0 = (1 - \rho_1)/[1 + k(1 - \rho_1)] \qquad \text{for } \rho = 1$$

For packets of source 1 the average time in A is

$$T_1 = (1/\mu)(1 + N)$$

where

$$N = \sum_{n=0}^{\infty} n p_n$$

is the average number in the system upon arrival. The average number in A from source 1 is

$$N_1 = \lambda_1 T_1$$

For packets of source 2 the average time in A is

$$T_2 = (1/\mu)(1 + N')$$

where

$$N' = \frac{\displaystyle\sum_{n=0}^{k-1} n p_n}{\displaystyle\sum_{n=0}^{k-1} p_n}$$

is the average number in the system found by an accepted packet of source 2. To find the average number in the system from source 2 we must find the arrival rate into node A of packets from source 2. This is

$$\lambda'_2 = \lambda_2 P\{\text{arriving packet from source 2 is accepted}\} = \lambda_2 \sum_{n=0}^{k-1} p_n$$

and the average number from source 2 in A is

$$N_2 = \lambda'_2 T_2$$

3.15

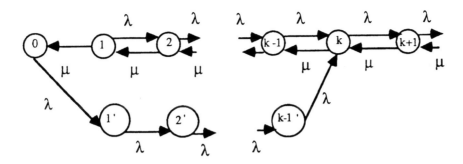

The transition diagram of the corresponding Markov chain is shown in the figure. We have introduced states 1', 2', . . ., (k-1)' corresponding to situations where there are customers in the system waiting for service to begin again after the system has emptied out. Using global balance equations between the set of states {1', 2', . . . ,i') and all other states, for i' = 1', . . . , (k-1)', we obtain $\lambda p_0 = \lambda p_{1'} = \lambda p_{2'} = \ldots = \lambda p_{(k-1)'}$, so

$$p_0 = p_{1'} = p_{2'} = \ldots = p_{(k-1)'}$$

Also by using global balance equations we have

$$\mu p_1 = \lambda p_0$$
$$\mu p_2 = \lambda(p_1 + p_{1'}) = \lambda(p_1 + p_0)$$
$$\cdot \quad \cdot \quad \cdot \quad \cdot \quad \cdot \quad \cdot \quad \cdot$$
$$\mu p_k = \lambda(p_{k-1} + p_{(k-1)'}) = \lambda(p_{k-1} + p_0)$$
$$\mu p_{i+1} = \lambda p_i \qquad\qquad\qquad i \geq k.$$

By denoting $\rho = \lambda/\mu$ we obtain

$$p_i = \rho(1 + \rho + \ldots + \rho^{i-1})p_0 \qquad\qquad 1 \leq i \leq k$$

$$p_i = \rho^{1+i-k}(1 + \rho + \ldots + \rho^{k-1})p_0 \qquad\qquad i > k.$$

Substituting these expressions in the equation $p_{1'} + \ldots + p_{(k-1)'} + p_0 + p_1 + \ldots = 1$ we obtain p_0

$$p_0\left(k + \sum_{i=1}^{k} \frac{\rho(1 - \rho^i)}{1 - \rho} + \frac{1 - \rho^k}{1 - \rho}\rho^2(1 + \rho + \ldots)\right) = 1$$

$$p_0 = \left(k + \frac{\rho}{1 - \rho}\sum_{i=1}^{k}(1 - \rho^i) + \frac{\rho^2}{(1 - \rho)^2}(1 - \rho^k)\right)^{-1}$$

After some calculation this gives $p_0 = (1 - \rho)/k$ (An alternative way to verify this formula is to observe that the fraction of time the server is busy is equal to ρ by Little's theorem). Therefore, the fraction of time the server is idle is $(1 - \rho)$. When this is divided among the k equiprobable states 0, 1', . . ., (k-1)' we obtain $p_0 = (1 - \rho)/k$. The average number in the system is

$$N = p_{1'} + 2p_{2'} + \dots + (k-1)p_{(k-1)'} + \sum_{i=0}^{\infty} ip_i = p_0 \frac{k(k-1)}{2} + \sum_{i=0}^{\infty} ip_i$$

where the probabilities p_i are given in the equations above. After some calculation this yields

$$N = (k-1)/2 + \rho/(1-\rho).$$

The average time in the system is (by Little's Theorem) $T = N/\lambda$.

3.16

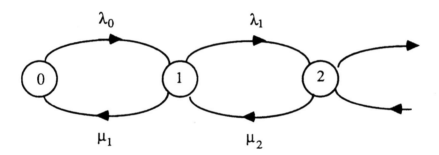

The figure shows the Markov chain corresponding to the given system. The local balance equation for it can be written down as :

$$\rho_0 P_0 = P_1$$

$$\rho_1 P_1 = P_2$$

$$\dots \qquad \dots$$

$$\Rightarrow P_{n+1} = \rho_n P_n = \rho_{n-1} \rho_n P_{n-1} = \dots = (\rho_0 \rho_1 \cdots \rho_n) P_0$$

but,

$$\sum_{i=0}^{\infty} P_i = P_0 (1 + \rho_0 + \rho_0 \rho_1 + \dots) = 1$$

$$\Rightarrow P_0 = \left[1 + \sum_{k=0}^{\infty} (\rho_0 \cdots \rho_k) \right]^{-1}$$

3.17

The discrete time version of the M/M/1 system can be characterized by the same Markov chain as the continuous time M/M/1 system and hence will have the same occupancy distribution.

3.18

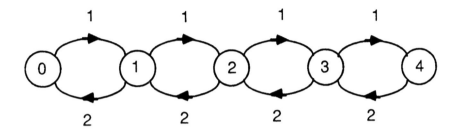

$$P_1 = \frac{1}{2} P_0$$

$$P_n = \frac{1}{2} P_{n-1} \quad \text{for } 1 \le n \le 4$$

$$\sum_{i=0}^{4} P_i = 1$$

Solving the above equations we get,

$$P_n = \frac{2^{4-n}}{31} \quad \text{for } 0 \le n \le 4$$

$$N = \sum_{n=0}^{4} n\, P_n = \frac{26}{31}$$

P(a customer arrives but has to leave) = 1/31

Hence the arrival rate of passengers who join the queue =

$$(1-p_4)\, \lambda = \frac{30}{31} \text{ per minute } = \lambda_a \text{ (say)}$$

$$T = N/\lambda_a = \frac{26/31}{30/31} = \frac{13}{15} \text{ minutes}$$

3.19

We have here an M/M/m/m system where m is the number of circuits provided by the company. Therefore we must find the smallest m for which $p_m < 0.01$ where p_m is given by the Erlang B formula

$$p_m = \frac{(\lambda/\mu)^m/m!}{\displaystyle\sum_{n=0}^{m}(\lambda/\mu)^n/n!}.$$

We have $\lambda = 30$ and $\mu = 1/3$, so $\lambda/\mu = 30 \cdot 3 = 90$. By substitution in the equation above we can calculate the required value of m.

3.20

We view this as an M/M/m problem. We have

$$\lambda = 0.5, \quad E(X) = 1/\mu = 3, \quad m = ? \text{ so that } W < 0.5$$

We know that the utilization factor has to be less than 1 or m has to be greater than or equal to 2. By the M/M/n results we have

$$W = \frac{\dfrac{\lambda}{m\mu} P_Q}{\lambda\left(1 - \dfrac{\lambda}{m\mu}\right)} = \frac{P_Q}{m\mu - \lambda}$$

$$\text{where } P_Q = \frac{P_0\left(\dfrac{\lambda}{\mu}\right)^m}{m!\left(1 - \dfrac{\lambda}{m\mu}\right)}$$

$$\text{and} \quad P_0 = \left[\sum_{n=0}^{m-1}\frac{(\lambda/\mu)^n}{n!} + \frac{(\lambda/\mu)^m}{m!\,(1-\lambda/\mu)}\right]^{-1}$$

As can be seen from the expressions above m should be at most 5 because at m=5 , W is less than 0.5 because P_Q is less than 1.

The following C program calculates the optimum m.

```
double P0(lambda,mu,m){
        mrho = lambda/mu;
        rho = mrho/m;
        for(n=0; n<m; n++)
                temp1 = pow(mrho,n)/ fact(n);
```

```
                temp2 = pow(mrho,m)/(fact(m)*(1-rho));
                return(1/( temp1 + temp2 )); /* this returns p₀ */
        }

        int  fact(n){
                if (n==0) return (1);
                else
                        return(n* fact (n-1));
        }

        double W(lambda,mu,m){
                PQ = P0(lambda,mu,m) * pow(mrho,m) /
                                        (fact(m) * (1-rho));
        return(PQ/(m *mu - lambda));
        }       /* this returns W for a given m */

        main() {
                lambda = 0.5; mu = 0.333; previous_W = 100.0;
                for(m=2; m<=5; m++)
                        if ((temp = W(lambda,mu,m)) < Previous_W)
                                previous_W = temp;
                        else
                                { print(m-1);
                                break;
                        }
        }
```

3.21

We have $p_n = \rho^n p_0$ where $\rho = \lambda/\mu$. Using the relation

$$\sum_{n=0}^{m} p_n = 1$$

we obtain

$$p_0 = \frac{1}{\sum_{n=0}^{m} \rho^n} = \frac{1-\rho}{1-\rho^{m+1}}$$

Thus

$$p_n = \frac{\rho^n(1-\rho)}{1-\rho^{m+1}}, \qquad 0 \le n \le m$$

3.22

(a) When all the courts are busy, the expected time between two departures is $40/5 = 8$ minutes. If a pair sees k pairs waiting in the queue, there must be exactly k+1 departures from the system before they get a court. Since all the courts would be busy during this whole time, the average waing time required before k+1 departures is 8(k+1) minutes.

(b) Let X be the expected waiting time given that the courts are found busy. We have

$$\lambda = 1/10, \qquad \mu = 1/40, \qquad \rho = \lambda/(5\mu) = 0.8$$

and by the M/M/m results

$$W = \frac{\rho P_Q}{\lambda(1 - \rho)}$$

Since $W = X P_Q$, we obtain $X = W/P_Q = \rho/[\lambda(1 - \rho)] = 40$ min.

3.23

Let

$$p_m = P\{\text{the 1st m servers are busy}\}$$

as given by the Erlang B formula. Denote

r_m = Arrival rate to servers (m+1) and above
λ_m = Arrival rate to server m.

We have

$$r_m = p_m \lambda$$
$$\lambda_m = r_{m-1} - r_m = (p_{m-1} - p_m)\lambda.$$

The fraction of time server m is busy is

$$b_m = \lambda_m/\mu.$$

3.24

We will show that the system is described by a Markov chain that is identical to the M/M/1 chain. For small δ we have

$$P\{k \text{ arrivals and } j \text{ departures}\} = 0(\delta) \qquad \text{if } k + j \geq 2$$

$$P\{0 \text{ arrivals and } 1 \text{ departure} \mid \text{starting state} = i \geq i\}$$
$$= P\{0 \text{ arrivals} \mid \text{starting state } i \geq 1\} \bullet P\{1 \text{ departure} \mid \text{starting state } i \geq 1\}$$

We have

$$P\{\,0 \text{ arrivals} \mid \text{starting state } i \geq 1\} = P\{0 \text{ arrivals}\} = 1 - \lambda\delta + 0(\delta).$$

The probability $P\{1 \text{ departure} \mid \text{starting state } i > 1\}$ is obtained from the binomial distribution or sum of i Bernoulli trials, each with a probability of success equal to $(\mu/i)\,\delta + 0(\delta)$. We need the probability of one success, which is

$$\binom{i}{1}(1-(\mu/i)\,\delta + 0(\delta))^{i-1}\,((\mu/i)\,\delta + 0(\delta))$$

Therefore

$$P\{\,0 \text{ arrivals and 1 departure} \mid \text{starting state} = i \geq 1\}$$
$$= \binom{i}{1}(1-(\mu/i)\,\delta + 0(\delta))^{i-1}\,((\mu/i)\,\delta + 0(\delta))\bullet(1-\lambda\delta + 0(\delta)) = \mu\delta + 0(\delta)$$

Similarly

$$P\{1 \text{ arrival and 0 departure} \mid \text{starting state} = i\}$$
$$= P\{1 \text{ arrival}\} \bullet P\{0 \text{ departure} \mid \text{starting state} = i\}$$

$$= (\lambda\delta + 0(\delta)) \bullet \left[\binom{i}{0}(1-(\mu/i)\,\delta + 0(\delta))^{i}\right] = \lambda\delta + 0(\delta)$$

Thus the transition rates are the same as for the M/M/1 system.

3.25

Let n_1 be the number of radio-to-radio calls and n_2 be the number of radio-to-nonradio calls which have not finished yet. Then we have the following Markov chain:

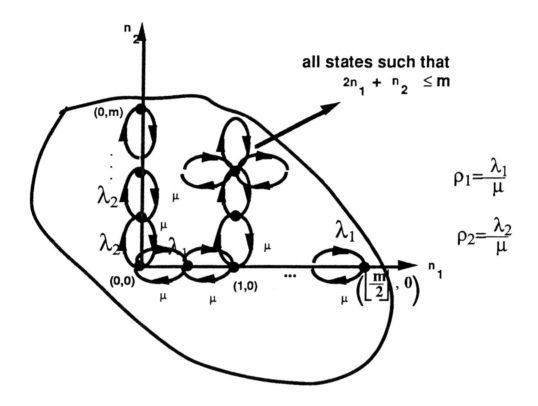

The occupancy distribution $p(n_1,n_2)$ is of the form

$$p(n_1,n_2) = \rho_1^{n_1}(1-\rho_1)\rho_2^{n_2}(1-\rho_2)/G, \quad \text{for } 2n_1+n_2 \leq m$$

and 0 otherwise (it is easy to check that this formula satisfies the global balance equations). To calculate G note that

$$\sum_{\{(n_1,n_2)|2n_1+n_2\leq m\}} \sum p(n_1,n_2) = 1 \Rightarrow G = \sum_{\{(n_1,n_2)|2n_1+n_2\leq m\}} \rho_1^{n_1}(1-\rho_1)\rho_2^{n_2}(1-\rho_2) =$$

$$\sum_{n_1=0}^{\lfloor\frac{m}{2}\rfloor}\sum_{n_2=0}^{m-2n_1}\rho_1^{n_1}(1-\rho_1)\rho_1^{n_2}(1-\rho_2) = \sum_{n_1=0}^{\lfloor\frac{m}{2}\rfloor} \rho_1^{n_1}(1-\rho_1)(1-\rho_2)\frac{1-\rho_2^{m-2n_1+1}}{1-\rho_2}$$

$$= (1-\rho_1)\sum_{n_1=0}^{\lfloor\frac{m}{2}\rfloor}\rho_1^{n_1} - \sum_{n_1=0}^{\lfloor\frac{m}{2}\rfloor}(1-\rho_1)\rho_2^{m+1}\left(\frac{\rho_1}{\rho_2^2}\right)^{n_1}$$

$$= 1 - \rho_1^{\left\lfloor \frac{m}{2} \right\rfloor + 1} - (1 - \rho_1)\rho_2^{m+1} \frac{1 - \left(\frac{\rho_1}{\rho_2^2}\right)^{\left\lfloor \frac{m}{2} \right\rfloor + 1}}{1 - \frac{\rho_1}{\rho_2^2}}$$

$$= 1 - \rho_1^{\left\lfloor \frac{m}{2} \right\rfloor + 1} - (1 - \rho_1)\rho_2^{m+1-2\left\lfloor \frac{m}{2} \right\rfloor} \frac{\rho_2^{2\left\lfloor \frac{m}{2} \right\rfloor + 2} - \rho_1^{\left\lfloor \frac{m}{2} \right\rfloor + 1}}{\rho_2^2 - \rho_1}$$

$$\Rightarrow G = \begin{cases} 1 - \rho_1^{\frac{m}{2}+1} - (1 - \rho_1)\rho_2 \dfrac{\rho_2^{m+2} - \rho_1^{m/2+1}}{\rho_2^2 - \rho_1} & \text{if } m \text{ even} \\[4ex] 1 - \rho_1^{\frac{m+1}{2}} - (1 - \rho_1)\rho_2^2 \dfrac{\rho_2^{m+1} - \rho_1^{\frac{m+1}{2}}}{\rho_2^2 - \rho_1} & \text{if } m \text{ odd} \end{cases}$$

Let

p_1 = blocking probability of radio-to-radio calls

p_2 = blocking probability of radio-to-nonradio calls

Then

$$P_2 = \sum_{2n_1 + n_2 = m} p(n_1, n_2)$$

$$P_1 = \sum_{m-1 \le 2n_1 + n_2 \le m} p(n_1, n_2) = p_2 + \sum_{2n_1 + n_2 = m-1} p(n_1, n_2).$$

But

$$P_2 = \sum_{n_1 = 0}^{\left\lfloor \frac{m}{2} \right\rfloor} p(n_1, m - 2n_1) = \sum_{n_1 = 0}^{\left\lfloor \frac{m}{2} \right\rfloor} \rho_1^{n_1}(1 - \rho_1)\rho_2^{m - 2n_1}(1 - \rho_2)/G =$$

$$= \frac{(1 - \rho_1)(1 - \rho_2)\rho_2^m}{G} \frac{1 - \left(\rho_1/\rho_2^2\right)^{\left\lfloor \frac{m}{2} \right\rfloor + 1}}{1 - \frac{\rho_1}{\rho_2^2}}$$

and

$$P_1 = P_2 + \sum_{n_1=0}^{\lfloor \frac{m-1}{2} \rfloor} p(n_1, m-1-2n_1) = P_2 + \frac{(1-\rho_1)(1-\rho_2)\rho_2^{m-1}}{G} \cdot \frac{1-\left(\frac{\rho_1}{\rho_2^2}\right)^{\lfloor \frac{m+1}{2} \rfloor}}{1-\frac{\rho_1}{\rho_2^2}}$$

3.26

Define the state to be the number of operational machines. This gives a Markov chain, which is the same as in an M/M/1/m queue with arrival rate λ and service rate μ. The required probability is simply p_0 for such a queue.

3.27

Assume $\mu_1 > \mu_2$.

We have the following Markov chain:

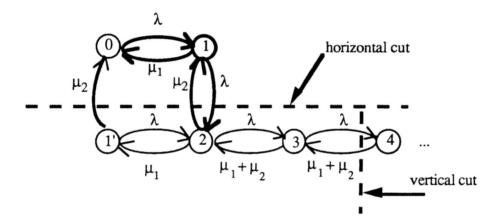

Let state 1 represent 1 customer in the system being served by server 1
Let state 1' represent 1 customer in the system being served by server 2

i) Flow across a vertical cut

$$p_i = \frac{\lambda}{\mu_1 + \mu_2} p_{i-1} \qquad \text{for } i \geq 2$$

Therefore

$$\overline{p_i} = \left(\frac{\lambda}{\mu_1 + \mu_2}\right)^{i-2} p_2 \qquad \text{for } i \geq 2$$

ii) Flow in and out of state 1'

$$(\lambda + \mu_2)\, p_{1'} = p_2\, \mu_1$$

Therefore

$$p_{1'} = p_2\, \frac{\mu_1}{\lambda + \mu_2}$$

iii) Flow across horizontal cut

$$p_1\, \lambda = (p_{1'} + p_2)\, \mu_2$$

Therefore

$$p_1 = \frac{\mu_2}{\lambda}\left(p_2 + p_2\, \frac{\mu_1}{\lambda + \mu_2}\right) = p_2\, \frac{\mu_2}{\lambda}\left(1 + \frac{\mu_1}{\lambda + \mu_2}\right)$$

iv) Flow in and out of state 0

$$p_0\, \lambda = \pi_1\, \mu_1 + p_{1'}\, \mu_2$$

Therefore

$$p_0 = \frac{1}{\lambda}\, p_2 \left(\frac{\mu_1\, \mu_2}{\lambda}\left(1 + \frac{\mu_1}{\lambda + \mu_2}\right) + \frac{\mu_1\, \mu_2}{\lambda + \mu_2}\right)$$

We have

$$\sum_i p_i = 1$$

from which

$$p_2 = \left(\frac{1}{1 - \dfrac{\lambda}{\mu_1 + \mu_2}} + \frac{\left(1 + (\mu_2/\lambda)\right)\mu_1}{\lambda + \mu_2} + \frac{\left(1 + (\mu_1/\lambda)\right)\mu_2}{\lambda}\left(1 + \frac{\mu_1}{\lambda + \mu_2}\right)\right)^{-1}$$

3.28

We have

$$E\{f^2\} = E\left\{\left(\sum_{i=1}^{n}\gamma_i\right)^2\right\} = E\left\{E\left\{\left(\sum_{i=1}^{n}\gamma_i\right)^2 \mid n\right\}\right\} = E\{ns_\gamma^2 + n(n-1)\Gamma^2\}$$

$$= E\{n\}(s_\gamma^2 - \Gamma^2) + E\{n^2\}\Gamma^2$$

Since

$$E\{n\} = \lambda/\mu, \qquad E\{n\} = \sigma_n^2 + (\lambda/\mu) = \lambda/\mu + (\lambda/\mu)$$

we obtain

$$\sigma_f^2 = E\{f^2\} - F^2 = E\{f^2\} - (\lambda/\mu)^2\Gamma^2 = (\lambda/\mu)(s_\gamma^2 - \Gamma^2) + [(\lambda/\mu) + (\lambda/\mu)^2]\Gamma^2 - (\lambda/\mu)^2\Gamma^2$$

$$= (\lambda/\mu)s_\gamma^2$$

so finally

$$\sigma_f = (\lambda/\mu)^{1/2}s_\gamma$$

3.29

For each value of x, the average customer waiting time for each of the two types of customers (x items or less, vs more than x) is obtained by the P-K formula for an M/G/1 system with arrival rate and service time parameters depending on x. By computing the overall customer waiting time for each x in the feasible range [1,40], we can numerically compute the optimal value of x.

Here is a program to find x to minimize the average waiting time:

```
Lambda=1; Past_T= 1000000; T=0; x=-1;
while (x<=40) do
if (T> Past_T) do
     begin
              Past_T = T;
              x = x+1;
              lambda1 = lambda * x/40;
              E_service_time_1 = (1+x)/2;
              E_service_time_2 = (41+x)/2;
              E_service_time_square1 = 0;
              E_service_time_square2 = 0;
              for i=1 to x do
                     E_service_time_square1 =
                     E_service_time_square1+(i*i);
```

```
                 for i=x+1 to 40 do
                        E_service_time_square2 =
                                E_service_time_square2+(i*i);
                 E_service_time_square1 =
                        E_service_time_square1/x;
                 E_service_time_square2 =
                                E_service_time_square2/(40-x);
                 T1 = E_service_time_1 +
                 (lambda*E_service_time_square1/(2.0*(1-
                 lambda1*E_service_time_1)));
                 T2 = E_service_time_2 +
                        (lambda*E_service_time_square2/(2.0*(1-
                                        lambda2*E_service_time_2)));
                 T = (T1*x + T2*(40-x))/40;
         end;
                 print(x);
```

3.30

From Little's Theorem (Example 1) we have that P{the system is busy} = $\lambda E\{X\}$.
Therefore P{the system is empty} = 1 - $\lambda E\{X\}$.

The length of an idle period is the interarrival time between two typical customer arrivals.
Therefore it has an exponential distribution with parameter λ, and its average length is $1/\lambda$.

Let B be the average length of a busy period and let I be the average length of an idle
period. By expressing the proportion of time the system is busy as B/(I + B) and also as
$\lambda E\{X\}$ we obtain

   $B = E\{X\}/(1 - \lambda E\{X\})$.

From this the expression $1/(1 - \lambda E\{X\})$ for the average number of customers served in a
busy period is evident.

3.31

The problem with the argument given is that more customers arrive while long-service
customers are served, so the average service time of a customer found in service by another
customer upon arrival is more than $E\{X\}$.

3.32

Following the hint we write for the ith packet

$$U_i = R_i + \sum_{j=1}^{N_i} X_{i-j}$$

where

    U_i : Unfinished work at the time of arrival of the ith customer
    R_i : Residual service time of the ith customer
    N_i : Number found in queue by the ith customer
    X_j : Service time of the jth customer

Hence

$$E\{U_i\} = E\{R_i\} + E\left\{ \sum_{j=1}^{N_i} E\{X_{i-j} \mid N_i\} \right\}$$

Since X_{i-j} and N_i are independent

$$E\{U_i\} = E\{R_i\} + E\{X\}E\{N_i\}$$

and by taking limit as $i \to \infty$ we obtain $U = R + (1/\mu)N_Q = R + (\lambda/\mu)W = R + \rho W$, so

$$W = (U - R)/\rho.$$

Now the result follows by noting that both U and R are independent of the order of customer service (the unfinished work is independent of the order of customer service, and the steady state mean residual time is also independent of the customer service since the graphical argument of Fig. 3.16 does not depend on the order of customer service).

3.33

Consider the limited service gated system with zero packet length and reservation interval equal to a slot. We have

    T_{TDM} = Waiting time in the gated system

For $E\{X^2\} = 0$, $E\{V\} = 1$, $\sigma_V^2 = 0$, $\rho = 0$ we have from the gated system formula (3.77)

    Waiting time in the gated system = $(m + 2 - 2\lambda)/(2(1 - \lambda)) = m/(2(1 - \lambda)) + 1$

which is the formula for T_{TDM} given by Eq. (3.59) .

3.34

(a) The system utilization is ρ, so the fraction of time the system transmits data is ρ. Therefore the portion of time occupied by reservation intervals is $1 - \rho$.

(b) If

p: Fraction of time a reservation interval is followed by an empty data interval

and M(t) is the number of reservation intervals up to time t, then the number of packets transmitted up to time t is $\approx (1 - p)M(t)$. The time used for reservation intervals is $\approx M(t)E\{V\}$, and for data intervals $\approx (1 - p)M(t)E\{X\}$. Since the ratio of these times must be $(1 - \rho)/\rho$ we obtain

$$(1 - \rho)/\rho = (M(t)E\{V\})/((1 - p)M(t)E\{X\}) = E\{V\}/((1 - p)E\{X\})$$

or

$$1 - p = (\rho E\{V\})/((1 - \rho)E\{X\})$$

which using $\lambda = \rho/E\{X\}$, yields $p = (1 - \rho - \lambda E\{V\})/(1 - \rho)$

3.35

Consider a gated all-at-once version of the limited service reservation system. Here there are m users, each with independent Poisson arrival rate λ/μ. Each user has a separate queue, and is allowed to make a reservation for at most one packet in each reservation interval. This packet is then transmitted in the subsequent data interval. The difference with the limited service system of Section 3.5.2 is that here users share reservation and data intervals.

Consider the ith packet arrival into the system and suppose that the user associated with packet i is user j. We have as in Section 3.5.2

$$E\{W_i\} = E\{R_i\} + E\{N_i\}/\mu + (1 + E\{Q_i\} - E\{m_i\})E\{V\}$$

where W_i, R_i, N_i, μ, $E\{V\}$ are as in Section 3.5.2, Q_i is the number of packets in the queue of user j found by packet i upon arrival, and m_i is the number (0 or 1) of packets of user j that will start transmission between the time of arrival of packet i and the end of the frame in which packet i arrives. We have as in Section 3.5.2

$$R = \lim_{i \to \infty} E\{R_i\} + E\{N_i\}/\mu + (1 + E\{Q_i\} - E\{m_i\})E\{V\}$$

$$N = \lim_{i \to \infty} E\{N_i\} = \lambda W$$

$$Q = \lim_{i \to \infty} E\{Q_i\} = \lambda W/m$$

so there remains to calculate $\lim_{i \to \infty} E\{m_i\}$.

There are two possibilities regarding the time of arrival of packet i.

a) Packet i arrives during a reservation interval. This event, call it A, has steady state probability (1-ρ)

$$P\{A\} = 1-\rho.$$

Since the ratio of average data interval length to average reservation interval length is ρ/(1-ρ) we see that the average steady state length of a data interval is ρE{V}/(1-ρ). Therefore the average steady state number of packets per user in a data interval is ρE{V}/((1-ρ)mE{X}) = λE{V}/((1-ρ)m). This also equals the steady state value of E{m$_i$| A} in view of the system symmetry with respect to users

$$\lim_{i \to \infty} E\{m_i| A\} = \frac{\lambda E\{V\}}{(1-\rho)m}.$$

b) Packet i arrives during a data interval. This event, call it B, has steady state probability ρ

$$P\{B\} = \rho.$$

Denote

$$\alpha = \lim_{i \to \infty} E\{m_i \mid B\},$$

$$\alpha_k = \lim_{i \to \infty} E\{m_i \mid B, \text{ the data interval of arrival of packet i contains k packets}\}.$$

Assuming k > 0 packets are contained in the data interval of arrival, there is equal probability 1/k of arrival during the transmission of any one of these packets. Therefore

$$\alpha_k = \sum_{n=1}^{k} \frac{1}{k} \frac{k-n}{m} = \frac{k(k-1)}{2km} = \frac{k-1}{m}.$$

Let P(k) be the unconditional steady-state probability that a nonempty data interval contains k packets, and E{k} and E{k^2} be the corresponding first two moments. Then we have using Bayes' rule

$$\lim_{i \to \infty} P\{\text{The data interval of arrival of packet i contains k packets}\} = kP(k)/E\{k\}.$$

Combining the preceding equations we have

$$\alpha = \sum_{k=1}^{m} \frac{kP(k)}{E\{k\}} \alpha_k = \sum_{k=1}^{m} \frac{P(k)k(k-1)}{2E\{k\}m} = \frac{E\{k^2\}}{2mE\{k\}} - \frac{1}{2m}.$$

We have already shown as part of the analysis of case a) above that

$$E\{k\} = \lambda E\{V\}/(1 - \rho)$$

so there remains to estimate $E\{k^2\}$. We have

$$E\{k^2\} = \sum_{k=1}^{m} k^2 P(k)$$

If we maximize the quantity above over the distribution $P(k)$, $k = 0,1,...,m$ subject to the constraints $\sum_{k=1}^{m} kP(k) = E\{k\}$, $\sum_{k=0}^{m} P(k) = 1$, $P(k) \geq 0$ (a simple linear programming problem) we find that the maximum is obtained for $P(m) = E\{k\}/m$, $P(0) = 1 - E\{k\}/m$, and $P(k) = 0$, $k = 1,2,...,m-1$. Therefore

$$E\{k^2\} \leq mE\{k\}.$$

Similarly if we minimize $E\{k^2\}$ subject to the same constraints we find that the minimum is obtained for $P(k'-1) = k' - E\{k\}$, $P(k) = 1 - (k' - E\{k\})$ and $P(k') = 0$ for $k \neq k' - 1$, k' where k' is the integer for which $k' - 1 \leq E\{k\} < k'$. Therefore

$$E\{k^2\} \geq (k' -1)^2(k' - E\{k\}) + (k')^2[1 - (k' - E\{k\})]$$

After some calculation this relation can also be written

$$E\{k^2\} \geq E\{k\} + (k' -1)(2E\{k\} - k') \text{ for } E\{k\} \in (k' - 1, k'),$$
$$k' = 1, 2, ..., m$$

Note that the lower bound above is a piecewise linear function of $E\{k\}$, and equals $(E\{k\})^2$ at the breakpoints $k' = 1,2,...,m$. Summarizing the bounds we have

$$\frac{E\{k\} + (k' - 1)(2E\{k\} - k')}{2mE\{k\}} - \frac{1}{2m} \leq \alpha \leq \frac{1}{2} - \frac{1}{2m} ,$$

where k' is the positive integer for which

$$k' - 1 \leq E\{k\} < k' .$$

Note that as $E\{k\}$ approaches its maximum value m (i.e., the system is heavily loaded), the upper and lower bounds coincide. By combining the results for cases a) and b) above we have

$$\lim_{i \to \infty} E\{m_i\} = P\{A\} \lim_{i \to \infty} E\{m_i| A\} + P\{B\} \lim_{i \to \infty} E\{m_i | B\}$$

$$= (1\text{-}\rho)\frac{\lambda E\{V\}}{(1-\rho)m} + \rho\alpha$$

or finally

$$\lim_{i\to\infty} E\{m_i\} = \frac{\lambda E\{V\}}{m} + \rho\alpha$$

where α satisfies the upper and lower bounds given earlier. By taking limit as $i \to \infty$ in the equation

$$E\{W_i\} = E\{R_i\} + E\{N_i\}/\mu + (1 + E\{Q_i\} - E\{m_i\})E\{V\}$$

and using the expressions derived we finally obtain

$$W = \frac{\lambda E\{X^2\}}{2\left(1-\rho - \dfrac{\lambda E\{V\}}{m}\right)} + \frac{(1-\rho)E\{V^2\}}{2\left(1-\rho - \dfrac{\lambda E\{V\}}{m}\right)E\{V\}} + \frac{\left(1 - \rho\alpha - \dfrac{\lambda E\{V\}}{m}\right)E\{V\}}{1-\rho - \dfrac{\lambda E\{V\}}{m}}$$

where α satisfies

$$\frac{E\{k\} + (k'-1)(2E\{k\} - k')}{2mE\{k\}} - \frac{1}{2m} \le \alpha \le \frac{1}{2} - \frac{1}{2m},$$

$E\{k\}$ is the average number of packets per data interval

$$E\{k\} = \lambda E\{V\}/(1-\rho)$$

and k' is the integer for which $k' - 1 \le E\{k\} < k'$. Note that the formula for the waiting time W becomes exact in the limit both as $\rho \to 0$ (light load), and as $\rho \to 1 - \lambda E\{V\}/m$ (heavy load) in which case $E\{k\} \to m$ and $\alpha \to 1/2 - 1/2m$. When m = 1 the formula for W is also exact and coincides with the one derived for the corresponding single user one-at-a-time limited service system.

3.36

For each session, the arrival rates, average transmission times and utilization factors for the short packets (class 1), and the long packets (class 2) are

$\lambda_1 = 0.25$ packets/sec,	$1/\mu_1 = 0.02$ secs,	$\rho_1 = 0.005$
$\lambda_2 = 2.25$ packets/sec,	$1/\mu_2 = 0.3$ secs,	$\rho_2 = 0.675$.

The corresponding second moments of transmission time are

$$E\{X_1^2\} = 0.0004 \qquad\qquad E\{X_2^2\} = 0.09.$$

The total arrival rate for each session is $\lambda = 2.5$ packets/sec. The overall 1st and 2nd moments of the transmission time, and overall utilization factors are given by

$$1/\mu = 0.1*(1/\mu_1) + 0.9*(1/\mu_2) = 0.272$$
$$E\{X^2\} = 0.1*E\{X_1^2\} + 0.9*E\{X_2^2\} = 0.081$$
$$\rho = \lambda/\mu = 2.5*0.272 = 0.68.$$

We obtain the average time in queue W via the P - K formula $W = (\lambda E\{X^2\})/(2*(1 - \rho)) = 0.3164$. The average time in the system is $T = 1/\mu + W = 0.588$. The average number in queue and in the system are $N_Q = \lambda W = 0.791$, and $N = \lambda T = 1.47$.

The quantities above correspond to each session in the case where the sessions are time - division multiplexed on the line. In the statistical multiplexing case W, T, N_Q and N are decreased by a factor of 10 (for each session).

In the nonpreemptive priority case we obtain using the corresponding formulas:

$$W_1 = (\lambda_1 E\{X_1^2\} + \lambda_2 E\{X_2^2\})/(2*(1 - \rho_1)) = 0.108$$
$$W_2 = (\lambda_1 E\{X_1^2\} + \lambda_2 E\{X_2^2\})/(2*(1 - \rho_1)*(1 - \rho_1 - \rho_2)) = 0.38$$
$$T_1 = 1/\mu_1 + W_1 = 0.128$$
$$T_2 = 1/\mu_2 + W_2 = 1.055$$
$$N_{Q1} = \lambda_1*W_1 = 0.027 \qquad\qquad N_{Q2} = \lambda_2*W_2 = 0.855$$
$$N_1 = \lambda_1*T_1 = 0.032 \qquad\qquad N_2 = \lambda_2*T_2 = 2.273.$$

3.37

(a)

$$\lambda = 1/60 \text{ per second}$$
$$E(X) = 16.5 \text{ seconds}$$
$$E(X^2) = 346.5 \text{ seconds}$$
$$T = E(X) + \lambda E(X^2)/2(1-\lambda E(X))$$
$$= 16.5 + (346.5/60)/2(1 - 16.5/60) = 20.48 \text{ seconds}$$

(b) Non-Preemptive Priority

In the following calculation, subscript 1 will imply the quantities for the priority 1 customers and 2 for priority 2 customers. Unsubscripted quantities will refer to the overall system.

$$\lambda = \frac{1}{60} \ , \quad \lambda_1 = \frac{1}{300} \ , \quad \lambda_2 = \frac{1}{75}$$

$$E(X) = 16.5 \ , \quad E(X_1) = 4.5 \ , \quad E(X_2) = 19.5$$

$$E(X^2) = 346.5$$

$$R = \frac{1}{2} \lambda E(X^2) = 2.8875$$

$$\rho_1 = \lambda_1 E(X_1) = 0.015$$

$$\rho_2 = \lambda_2 E(X_2) = 0.26$$

$$W_1 = \frac{R}{1-\rho_1} = 2.931$$

$$W_2 = \frac{R}{1-\rho_2} = 4.043$$

$$T_1 = 7.4315, \quad T_2 = 23.543$$

$$T = \frac{\lambda_1 T_1 + \lambda_2 T_2}{\lambda} = 20.217$$

(c) Preemptive Queueing

The arrival rates and service rates for the two priorities are the same for preemptive system as the non-preemptive system solved above.

$$E(X_1^2) = 22.5, \quad E(X_2^2) = 427.5$$

$$R_1 = \frac{1}{2} \lambda_1 E(X_1^2) = 0.0075$$

$$R_2 = R_1 + \frac{1}{2} \lambda_2 E(X_2^2) = 2.8575$$

$$T_1 = \frac{E(X_1)(1-\rho_1) + R_1}{1-\rho_1}$$

$$T_2 = \frac{E(X_2)(1-\rho_1-\rho_2) + R_2}{(1-\rho_1)(1-\rho_1-\rho_2)}$$

$$T = (\lambda_1 T_1 + \lambda_2 T_2)/\lambda = 19.94$$

3.38

(a) The same derivation as in Section 3.5.3 applies for W_k, i.e.

$$W_k = R/(1 - \rho_1 - \ldots - \rho_{k-1})(1 - \rho_1 - \ldots - \rho_k)$$

where $\rho_i = \lambda_i/(m\mu)$, and R is the mean residual service time. Think of the system as being comprised of a serving section and a waiting section. The residual service time is just the time until any of the customers in the waiting section can enter the serving section. Thus, the residual service time of a customer is zero if the customer enters service immediately because there is a free server at the time of arrival, and is otherwise equal to the time between the customer's arrival, and the first subsequent service completion. Using the memoryless property of the exponential distribution it is seen that

$$R = P_Q E\{\text{Residual service time} \mid \text{queueing occurs}\} = P_Q/(m\mu).$$

(b) The waiting time of classes $1, \ldots, k$ is not influenced by the presence of classes $(k+1), \ldots, n$. All priority classes have the same service time distribution, thus, interchanging the order of service does not change the average waiting time. We have

$$W_{(k)} = \text{Average waiting time for the M/M/m system with rate } \lambda_1 + \ldots + \lambda_k.$$

By Little's theorem we have

$$\text{Average number in queue of class k} = \text{Average number in queue of classes 1 to k}$$
$$- \text{Average number in queue of classes 1 to k-1}$$

and the desired result follows.

3.39

Let k be such that

$$\rho_1 + \ldots + \rho_{k-1} \le 1 < \rho_1 + \ldots + \rho_k.$$

Then the queue of packets of priority k will grow infinitely, the arrival rate of each priority up to and including k-1 will be accomodated, the departure rate of priorities above k will be zero while the departure rate of priority k will be

$$\tilde{\lambda}_k = \frac{(1 - \rho_1 - \cdots - \rho_{k-1})}{X_k}$$

In effect we have a priority system with k priorities and arrival rates

$$\tilde{\lambda}_i = \lambda_i \qquad \text{for } i < k$$

$$\tilde{\lambda}_k = \frac{(1 - \rho_1 - \cdots - \rho_{k-1})}{\overline{X}_k}$$

For priorities $i < k$ the arrival process is Poisson so the same calculation for the waiting time as before gives

$$W_i = \frac{\displaystyle\sum_{i=1}^{k} \tilde{\lambda}_i \overline{X_i^2}}{2(1 - \rho_1 - \cdots - \rho_{i-1})(1 - \rho_1 - \cdots - \rho_i)}, \qquad i < k$$

For priority k and above we have infinite average waiting time in queue.

3.40

(a) The algebraic verification using Eq. (3.79) listed below

$$W_k = R/(1 - \rho_1 - \ldots - \rho_{k-1})(1 - \rho_1 - \ldots - \rho_k)$$

is straightforward. In particular by induction we show that

$$\rho_1 W_1 + \cdots + \rho_k W_k = \frac{R(\rho_1 + \quad + \rho_k)}{1 - \rho_1 - \cdots - \rho_k}$$

The induction step is carried out by verifying the identity

$$\rho_1 W_1 + \cdots + \rho_k W_k + \rho_{k+1} W_{k+1} = \frac{R(\rho_1 + \cdots + \rho_k)}{1 - \rho_1 - \cdots - \rho_k} + \frac{\rho_{k+1} R}{(1 - \rho_1 - \cdots \rho_k)(1 - \rho_1 - \cdots - \rho_{k+1})}$$

The alternate argument suggested in the hint is straightforward.

(b) Cost

$$C = \sum_{k=1}^{n} c_k N_Q^k = \sum_{k=1}^{n} c_k \lambda_k W_k = \sum_{k=1}^{n} \left(\frac{c_k}{\overline{X}_k}\right) \rho_k W_k$$

We know that $W_1 \le W_2 \le \ldots \le W_n$. Now exchange the priority of two neighboring classes i and $j = i+1$ and compare C with the new cost

$$C' = \sum_{k=1}^{n} \left(\frac{c_k}{\overline{X}_k}\right) \rho_k W'_k$$

In C' all the terms except $k = i$ and j will be the same as in C because the interchange does not affect the waiting time for other priority class customers. Therefore

$$C'-C = \frac{c_j}{X_j}\rho_j W'_j + \frac{c_i}{X_i}\rho_i W'_i - \frac{c_i}{X_i}\rho_i W_i - \frac{c_j}{X_j}\rho_j W_j.$$

We know from part (a) that

$$\sum_{k=1}^{n} \rho_k W_k = \text{constant.}$$

Since W_k is unchanged for all k except $k = i$ and j ($= i+1$) we have

$$\rho_i W_i + \rho_j W_j = \rho_i W'_i + \rho_j W'_j.$$

Denote

$$B = \rho_i W'_i - \rho_i W_i = \rho_j W_j - \rho_j W'_j$$

Clearly we have $B \geq 0$ since the average waiting time of customer class i will be increased if class i is given lower priority. Now let us assume that

$$\frac{c_i}{X_i} \leq \frac{c_j}{X_j}$$

Then

$$C'-C = \frac{c_i}{X_i}(\rho_i W'_i - \rho_i W_i) - \frac{c_j}{X_j}(\rho_j W_j - \rho_j W'_j) = B\left(\frac{c_i}{X_i} - \frac{c_j}{X_j}\right)$$

Therefore, only if $\frac{c_i}{X_i} < \frac{c_{i+1}}{X_{i+1}}$ can we reduce the cost by exchanging the priority order of i and i+1. Thus, if (1,2,3,...,n) is an optimal order we must have

$$\frac{c_1}{X_1} \geq \frac{c_2}{X_2} \geq \frac{c_3}{X_3} \geq \ldots \geq \frac{c_n}{X_n}$$

3.41

Let $D(t)$ and $T_i(t)$ be as in the solution of Problem 3.31. The inequality in the hint is evident from Figure 3.30, and therefore it will suffice to show that

$$\lim_{t \to \infty} \frac{1}{t} \sum_{i \in D(t)} T_i = \lim_{t \to \infty} \frac{1}{t} \sum_{i=1}^{\alpha(t)} T_i \qquad (1)$$

We first show that

$$T_k/t_k \to 0 \qquad \text{as } k \to \infty \qquad (2)$$

where t_k is the arrival time of the kth customer. We have by assumption

$$\lim_{k \to \infty} (k/t_k) = \lambda,$$

and by taking the limit as $k \to \infty$ in the relation

$$(k+1)/t_{k+1} - k/t_k = 1/t_{k+1} - ((t_{k+1} - t_k)/t_{k+1})(k/t_k)$$

we obtain

$$t_k/t_{k+1} \to 1 \qquad \text{as } k \to \infty \qquad (3)$$

We also have

$$\frac{\sum_{i=1}^{k} T_i}{t_k} = \frac{k}{t_k} \frac{\sum_{i=1}^{k} T_i}{k} \to \lambda T \qquad \text{as } k \to \infty \qquad (4)$$

so

$$\frac{\sum_{i=1}^{k+1} T_i}{t_{k+1}} - \frac{\sum_{i=1}^{k} T_i}{t_k} \to 0$$

or

$$\frac{T_{k+1}}{t_{k+1}} + \frac{\sum_{i=1}^{k} T_i}{t_k} (\frac{t_k}{t_{k+1}} - 1) \to 0$$

which proves (2).

Let $\varepsilon > 0$ be given. Then, from (2), there exists k such that $T_i < t_i \, \varepsilon$ for all $i > k$. Choose t large enough so that $\alpha(t) > k$. Then

$$\sum_{i=1}^{\beta(t)} M_i \le \int_0^t r(\tau)d\tau \le \sum_{i=1}^{\alpha(t)} M_i$$

or

$$\frac{\beta(t)}{t}\frac{\sum_{i=1}^{\beta(t)} M_i}{\beta(t)} \le \frac{1}{t}\int_0^t r(\tau)d\tau \le \frac{\alpha(t)}{t}\frac{\sum_{i=1}^{\alpha(t)} M_i}{\alpha(t)}$$

Under the assumptions

$$\lambda = \lim_{t\to\infty}\frac{\alpha(t)}{t} = \lim_{t\to\infty}\frac{\beta(t)}{t}$$

$$M = \lim_{k\to\infty}\frac{1}{k}\sum_{i=1}^k M_i$$

we have

$$R = \lambda M$$

where

$$R = \lim_{t\to\infty}\frac{1}{t}\int_0^t r(\tau)d\tau$$

is the time average rate at which the system earns.

(b) Take $r_i(t) = 1$ for all t for which customer i resides in the system, and $r_i(t) = 0$ for all other t.

(c) If X_i and W_i are the service and queueing times of the ith customer we have

$$M_i = X_i W_i + (X_i^2)/2$$

where the two terms on the right above correspond to payment while in queue and service respectively. Applying part (a) while taking expected values and taking the limit as $i \to \infty$, and using the fact that X_i and W_i are independent we obtain

$$U = \lambda(E\{X\}W + E\{(X_i^2)/2\})$$

where U, the rate at which the system earns, is the average unfinished work in the system. Since the arrival process is Poisson, U is also the average unfinished work seen by an arriving customer. Therefore U = W, and the P = K formula follows.

3.43

We have similar to Section 3.5

$$W = R + \rho W + \overline{W}_B \qquad (1)$$

where the mean residual service time is

$$R = \frac{\lambda \bar{n} \overline{X^2}}{2}$$

We derive the average waiting time of a customer for other customers that arrived in the same batch

$$\overline{W}_B = \sum_j r_j E\{W_B \mid \text{batch has size } j\}$$

where

P_j = Probability a batch has size j
r_j = Proportion of customers arriving in a batch of size j

We have

$$r_j = \frac{jP_j}{\displaystyle\sum_{n=1}^{\infty} nP_n} = \frac{jP_j}{\bar{n}}$$

Also since the customer is equally likely to be in any position within the batch

$$E\{W_B \mid \text{batch is of size } j\} = \sum_{k=1}^{j} (k - 1)\overline{X}\frac{1}{j} = \frac{j-1}{2}\overline{X}$$

Thus from (2)

$$E\{W_B\} = \sum_j \frac{jP_j(j-1)\overline{X}}{2\bar{n}} = \frac{\overline{X}(\overline{n^2} - \bar{n})}{2\bar{n}}$$

Substituting in (1) we obtain

$$W = \frac{R}{1-\rho} + \frac{\overline{W}_B}{1-\rho}$$

$$= \frac{\lambda \overline{n} \overline{X^2}}{2(1-\rho)} + \frac{\overline{x}(\overline{n^2} - \overline{n})}{2\overline{n}(1-\rho)}$$

3.44

(a) Let p_0 be the steady state probability that an arriving packet finds the system empty. Then, in effect, a packet has service time X with probability $1 - p_0$, and service time $X + \Delta$ with probability p_0. The fraction of time the system is busy is obtained by applying Little's Theorem to the service portion of the system

$$\lambda[E\{X\}(1 - p_0) + (E\{X\} + E\{\Delta\})p_0] = \lambda(E\{X\} + E\{\Delta\}p_0)$$

This is also equal to P{system busy} $= 1 - p_0$, so by solving for p_0, we obtain

$$p_0 = (1 - \lambda E\{X\})/(1 + \lambda E\{\Delta\}) = (1 - \rho)/(1 + \lambda E\{\Delta\})$$

where $\rho = \lambda E\{X\}$.

(b) Let

E{I} = average length of an idle period
E{B} = average length of a busy period

Since the arrival process is Poisson we have

$E\{I\} = 1/\lambda$ = average time betwen last departure in a busy period and the next arrival in the system

$$p_0 = \frac{E\{I\}}{E\{I\} + E\{B\}} = \frac{1/\lambda}{1/\lambda + E\{B\}} = \frac{1 - \lambda E\{X\}}{1 + \lambda E\{\Delta\}}$$

$$E\{B\} = \frac{E\{X\} + E\{\Delta\}}{1 - E\{X\}\lambda} = \frac{E\{X\} + E\{\Delta\}}{1 - \rho}$$

(c) We calculate the mean residual time using a graphical argument

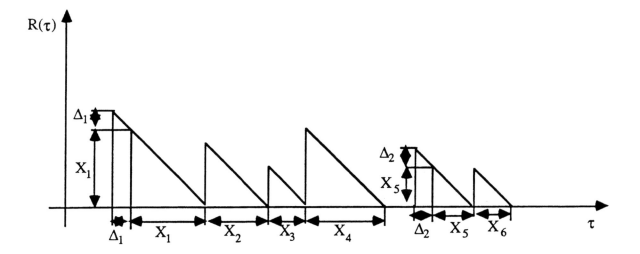

From the figure we have

$$\int_0^t R(\tau)d\tau = \sum_{i=1}^{M(t)}\frac{1}{2}X_i^2 + \sum_{i=1}^{N(t)}X_{j(i)}\Delta_i + \frac{1}{2}\Delta_i^2$$

where $X_{j(i)}$ is the service time of the first packet of the ith busy period, and

$M(t)$ = # of arrivals up to t
$N(t)$ = # of busy periods up to t

Taking the limit as $t \to \infty$, and using the fact

$$\lim_{t\to\infty}\frac{N(t)}{t} = \frac{1-p_0}{E\{B\}} = \frac{\lambda(1-\rho)}{1+\lambda E\{\Delta\}}$$

we obtain

$$R = \lim_{t\to\infty}\frac{\int_0^t R(\tau)d\tau}{t} = \lim_{t\to\infty}\left[\frac{M(t)}{t}\frac{\sum_{i=1}^{M(t)}\frac{1}{2}X_i^2}{M(t)} + \frac{N(t)}{t}\frac{\sum_{i=1}^{N(t)}X_{j(i)}\Delta_i + \frac{1}{2}\Delta_i^2}{N(t)}\right]$$

We have, as in Section 3.5, $W = R + \rho W$ or

$$W = R/(1-\rho)$$

Substituting the expression for R obtained previously we obtain

$$W = \frac{\lambda E\{X^2\}}{2(1-\rho)} + \frac{\lambda}{2(1+\lambda E\{\Delta\})}[E\{(X+\Delta)^2\} - E\{X^2\}]$$

3.45

(a) It is easy to see that

Pr (system busy serving customers) = ρ

Pr (system idle) = 1-ρ = P(0 in system) + P(1 in idle system) + ...
+ P(k-1 in idle system)

It can be seen that

P(0 in system) = P(1 in idle system) = ... = P(k-1 in idle system) = $(1-\rho)/k$

implying that

$$\text{P(nonempty and waiting)} = \frac{(1-\rho)(k-1)}{k}$$

(b) A busy period in this problem is the length of time the system is nonempty. The end of each busy period is a renewal point for the system. Between two renewal points, the system is either waiting (with 0 or more customers) or serving.

Let $\overline{W}$ be the expected length of a waiting period. Since arrivals are poisson, we have

$$\overline{W} = \frac{k}{\lambda} \ .$$

Let $\overline{S}$ be the expected length of a serving period. Then the probability that the system is serving = $\rho = \dfrac{\overline{S}}{\overline{S} + \overline{W}}$

implying that

$$\frac{1}{\rho} - 1 = \frac{\overline{W}}{\overline{S}}$$

or

$$\overline{S} = \frac{\rho \overline{W}}{1-\rho} = \frac{\rho \frac{k}{\lambda}}{1-\rho}$$

Let $\bar{I}$ be the expected length of time the system is empty.

The expected length of a busy period $= \bar{S} + \bar{W} - \bar{I}$

$$= \frac{\rho(k/\lambda)}{1-\rho} + \frac{k}{\lambda} - \frac{1}{\lambda}$$

$$= \frac{\rho k + (1-\rho)(k-1)}{\lambda(1-\rho)} = \frac{k + \rho - 1}{\lambda(1-\rho)}$$

$\frac{\rho(k/\lambda)}{1-\rho}$ is k times the average length of an M/G/1 busy period and $\frac{k-1}{\lambda}$

is the average time from the first arrival until the system starts serving.

(c) We will call the k packets that are in the system at the beginning of the busy period "old" packets. Those that come during the busy period (and are therefore served during this period) are called "new" packets.

We consider the following service discipline: the server transmits old packets only when it doesn't have new packets available at that moment (so it's not FCFS). Since this discipline doesn't depend on the length of the packets it will give the same average number of packets in the system. Thus a busy period looks as illustrated below:

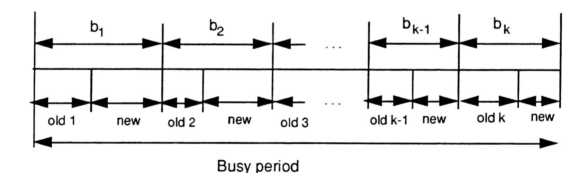

Busy period

In a subperiod b_i of the busy period, the old packet i and the new packets combine to give the same distribution as a normal M/G/1 busy period except that there are an extra k-i old packets in the system. It is easy to see that the distribution of the length of $b_1, b_2, \ldots b_k$ is the same since each of them is exactly like an M/G/1 busy period.

$$\Rightarrow E(N \mid serving) = E(N \mid b_1) P(b_1 \mid serving) + \ldots + E(N \mid b_k) P(b_k \mid serving)$$

$$P(b_i \mid serving) = \frac{1}{k}$$

$$E(N \mid b_i) = E(N_{M/G/1} \mid busy) + k-i$$

implying that

$$E(N \mid serving) = \frac{1}{k}\left(k\ E(N_{M/G/1} \mid busy) + \sum_{i=1}^{k}(k-i)\right)$$

$$= \frac{k-1}{2} + E(N_{M/G/1} \mid busy)$$

We have

$$E(N_{M/G/1}) = E(N_{M/G/1} \mid busy)\ \rho$$

from which

$$E(N_{M/G/1} \mid busy) = \frac{E(N_{M/G/1})}{\rho}$$

or

$$E(N \mid serving) = \frac{E(N_{M/G/1})}{\rho} + \frac{k-1}{2}$$

Also

$$E(N \mid busy\ waiting) = E(N \mid waiting\ with\ 1)\ P(waiting\ with\ 1 \mid busy\ waiting) + ...$$

$$+ E(N \mid waiting\ with\ k-1)\ P(waiting\ with\ k-1 \mid busy\ waiting)$$

$$P(waiting\ with\ i \mid busy\ waiting)$$

$$= P(waiting\ with\ j \mid busy\ waiting) = \frac{1}{k-1} \quad \text{for all } 0 < i, j < k$$

from which

$$E(N \mid busy\ waiting) = \frac{1}{k-1}\sum_{i=1}^{k-1}i \ \ = \frac{k}{2}$$

(d) $E(N) = E(N \mid busy\ waiting)\ P(busy\ waiting) + E(N \mid busy\ serving)\ P(busy\ serving)$

$$= \frac{k}{2}\ \frac{(k-1)\ (1-\rho)}{k} + \left(\frac{E(N_{M/G/1})}{\rho} + \frac{k-1}{2}\right)\rho$$

$$= E(N_{M/G/1}) + \frac{k-1}{2}$$

3.46

We have

$$W = R/(1 - \rho)$$

where

$$R = \lim_{t \to \infty} \left\{ \frac{1}{t} \sum_{i=1}^{M(t)} \frac{1}{2} X_i^2 + \frac{1}{t} \sum_{i=1}^{L(t)} \frac{V_i^2}{2} \right\}$$

where L(t) is the number of vacations (or busy periods) up to time t. The average length of an idle period is

$$I = \int_0^\infty p(v) \left[\int_0^V v \lambda e^{-\lambda \tau} d\tau + \int_V^\infty \tau \lambda e^{-\lambda \tau} d\tau \right] dv$$

and it can be seen that the steady-state time average number of vacations per unit time

$$\lim_{t \to \infty} \frac{L(t)}{t} = \frac{1 - \rho}{I}$$

We have

$$\lim_{t \to \infty} \frac{1}{t} \sum_{i=1}^{L(t)} \frac{V_i^2}{2} = \lim_{t \to \infty} \frac{L(t)}{t} \frac{\sum_{i=1}^{L(t)} \frac{V_i^2}{2}}{L(t)} = \lim_{t \to \infty} \frac{L(t)}{t} \frac{\overline{V^2}}{2I} = \frac{\overline{V^2}(1 - \rho)}{2I}$$

Therefore

$$R = \frac{\lambda \overline{X^2}}{2} + \frac{\overline{V^2}(1 - \rho)}{2I}$$

and

$$W = \frac{\lambda \overline{X^2}}{2(1 - \rho)} + \frac{\overline{V^2}}{2I}$$

3.47

(a) Since arrival times and service times are independent, the probability that there was an arrival in a small interval δ at time $\tau - x$ and that this arrival is still being served at time τ is $\lambda \delta [1 - F_X(x)]$.

(b) We have

$$\overline{X} = \int_0^\infty x dF_X(x)$$

and by calculating the shaded area of the figure below in two different ways we obtain

$$\int_0^\infty x dF_X(x) = \int_0^\infty [1 - F_X(x)]dx$$

This proves the desired expression.

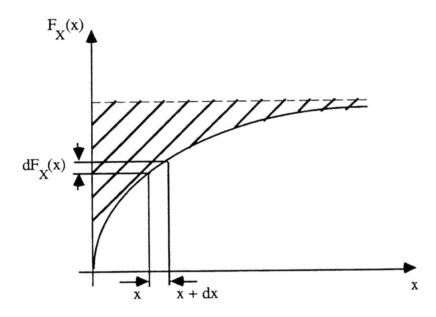

(c) Let $p_n(x)$ be the steady state probability that the number of arrivals that occurred prior to time $\tau - x$ and are still present at time τ is exactly n.

For $n \geq 1$ we have

$$p_n(x - \delta) = \{1 - \lambda[1 - F_X(x)]\delta\}p_n(x) + \lambda[1 - F_X(x)]\delta p_{n-1}(x)$$

and for $n = 0$ we have

$$p_0(x - \delta) = \{1 - \lambda[1 - F_X(x)]\delta\}p_0(x).$$

Thus $p_n(x)$, $n = 0, 1, 2, \ldots$ are the solution of the differential equations

$$dp_n/dx = a(x)p_n(x) - a(x)p_{n-1}(x) \qquad \text{for } n \geq 1$$

$$dp_0/dx = a(x)p_0(x) \qquad\qquad \text{for } n = 0$$

where

$$a(x) = \lambda[1 - F_X(x)].$$

Using the known conditions

$$p_n(\infty) = 0 \qquad \text{for } n \geq 1$$
$$p_0(\infty) = 1$$

it can be verified by induction starting with $n = 0$ that the solution is

$$p_n(x) = [e^{-\int_x^\infty a(y)dy}] \frac{[\int_x^\infty a(y)dy]^n}{n!}, \qquad x \geq 0, \ n = 0, 1, 2, \ldots$$

Since

$$\int_0^\infty a(y)dy = \lambda \int_0^\infty [1 - F_X(x)]dy = \lambda E\{X\}$$

we obtain

$$p_n(0) = e^{-\lambda E\{X\}} \frac{[\lambda E\{X\}]^n}{n!}, \qquad\qquad n = 0, 1, 2, \ldots$$

Thus the number of arrivals that are still in the system have a steady state Poisson distribution with mean $\lambda E\{X\}$.

3.48

(a) Denote

$$f(x) = E_r[(\max\{0, r-x\})^2]$$

and

$$g(x) = (E_r[\max\{0, r-x\}])^2,$$

where $E_r[\cdot]$ denotes expected value with respect to r (x is considered constant). We will prove that $f(x)/g(x)$ is montonically nondecreasing for x nonnegative and thus attain its minimum value for $x=0$. We have

$$\frac{\partial f(x)}{\partial x} = E_r\left[\frac{\partial}{\partial x}(\max\{0,r\text{-}x\})^2\right] = 2E_r\left[\max\{0,r\text{-}x\}\cdot\frac{\partial}{\partial x}(\max\{0,r\text{-}x\})\right],$$

where

$$\frac{\partial(\max\{0,r\text{-}x\})}{\partial x} = -u(r\text{-}x)$$

where $u(\cdot)$ is the step function. Thus

$$\frac{\partial f(x)}{\partial x} = -2E_r\left[(\max\{0,r\text{-}x\})\cdot u(r\text{-}x)\right] = -2E_r[\max\{0,r\text{-}x\}]$$

Assume for simplicity that r has a probability density function (the solution is similar in the more general case). Then

$$\frac{\partial g(x)}{\partial x} = 2E_r[\max\{0,r\text{-}x\}] E_r\left[\frac{\partial}{\partial x}\max\{0,r\text{-}x\}\right] = -2E_r[\max\{0,r\text{-}x\}]\cdot\int_{r>x}p(r)dr$$

Thus

$$\frac{\partial f(x)}{\partial x}g(x) - f(x)\frac{\partial g(x)}{\partial x} = 2E_r[\max\{0,r\text{-}x\}]E_r\left[(\max\{0,r\text{-}x\})^2\right]\int_{r>x}p(r)dr$$

$$- 2E_r[\max\{0,r\text{-}x\}]E_r([\max\{0,r\text{-}x\}])^2$$

For $\frac{f(x)}{g(x)}$ monotonically nondecreasing we must have $\frac{\partial f(x)}{\partial x}g(x) - f(x)\frac{\partial g(x)}{\partial x} \geq 0$ or equivalently

$$E_r[(\max\{0,r\text{-}x\})^2]\int_{r>x}p(r)dr - (E_r[\max\{0,r\text{-}x\}])^2$$

$$= \int_{r>x}(r\text{-}x)^2 p(r)dr \int_{r>x}p(r)dr - \left(\int_{r>x}(r\text{-}x)p(r)dr\right)^2 \geq 0$$

which is true by Schwartz's inequality. Thus the ratio

$$\frac{f(x)}{g(x)} = \frac{E_r[(\max\{0,r\text{-}x\})^2]}{(E_r[\max\{0,r\text{-}x\}])^2}$$

is monotonically nondecreasing and attains its minimum value at x=0. On the other hand, we have

$$\frac{f(0)}{g(0)} = \frac{E(r^2)}{[E(r)]^2},$$

since $r \geq 0$, and the result follows.

(b) We know (cf. Eq. (3.93)) that

$$I_k = - \min\{0, W_k + X_k - \tau_k\} = \max\{0, \tau_k - W_k - X_k\}$$

$$= \max\{0, \tau_k - S_k\},$$

where S_k is the time in the system. Since the relation in part (a) holds for any nonnegative scalar x, we can take expected values with respect to x as well, and use the fact that for any function of x, g(x), $E(g(x)^2) \geq E^2(g(x))$, and find that

$$E_{\tau,x}[(\max\{0, r-x\})^2] \geq \frac{\overline{r^2}}{(\overline{r^2})} (E_{\tau,x}[\max\{0, r-x\}])^2, \tag{1}$$

where x is considered to be a random variable this time. By letting $r = \tau_k$, $x = S_k$, and $k \to \infty$, we find from (1) that

$$\overline{I^2} \geq \frac{\overline{\tau^2}}{(\overline{\tau})^2} (\overline{I})^2$$

or

$$\frac{\overline{I^2} - (\overline{I})^2}{(\overline{I})^2} \geq \frac{\overline{\tau^2} - (\overline{\tau})^2}{(\overline{\tau})^2}$$

or

$$\sigma_I^2 \geq \frac{(\overline{I})^2}{(\overline{\tau})^2} \sigma_a^2 \quad \text{(since } \sigma_a^2 \text{ is defined as the variance of interarrival times)}$$

Since $\overline{I} = \frac{1-\rho}{\lambda}$ and $\overline{\tau} = \frac{1}{\lambda}$ we get

$$\sigma_I^2 \geq (1-\rho)^2 \sigma_a^2$$

By using Eq. (3.97), we then obtain

$$W \leq \frac{\lambda(\sigma_a^2 + \sigma_b^2)}{2(1-\rho)} - \frac{\lambda(1-\rho)\sigma_a^2}{2}$$

3.49

(a) Since the arrivals are Poisson with rate λ, the mean time until the next arrival starting from any given time (such as the time when the system becomes empty) is $1/\lambda$. The time average fraction of busy time is $\lambda E[X]$. This can be seen by Little's theorem applied to the service facility (the time average number of customers in the server is just the time average fraction of busy time), or it can be seen by letting $\sum_{i=1}^{n} X_i$ represent the time the server is busy with the first n customers, dividing by the arrival time of the nth customer, and going to the limit.

Let $E[B]$ be the mean duration of a busy period and $E[I] = 1/\lambda$ be the mean duration of an idle period. The time average fraction of busy time must be $E[B]/(E[B]+E[I])$. Thus

$$\lambda E[X] = E[B]/(E[B]+1/\lambda) ; \qquad E[B] = \frac{E[X]}{1 - \lambda E[X]}$$

This is the same as for the FCFS M/G/1 system (Problem 3.30).

(b) If a second customer arrives while the first customer in a busy period is being served, that customer (and all subsequent customers that arrive while the second customer is in the system) are served before the first customer resumes service. The same thing happens for any subsequent customer that arrives while the first customer is actually in service. Thus when the first customer leaves, the system is empty. One can view the queue here as a stack, and the first customer is at the bottom of the stack. It follows that $E[B]$ is the expected system time given a customer arriving to an empty system.

The customers already in the system when a given customer arrives receive no service until the given customer departs. Thus the system time of the given customer depends only on its own service time and the new customers that arrive while the given customer is in the system. Because of the memoryless property of the Poisson arrivals and the independence of service times, the system time of the given customer is independent of the number of customers (and their remaining service times) in the system when the given customer arrives. Since the expected system time of a given customer is independent of the number of customers it sees upon arrival in the system, the expected time is equal to the expected system time when the given customer sees an empty system; this is $E[B]$ as shown above.

(c) Given that a customer requires 2 units of service time, look first at the expected system time until 1 unit of service is completed. This is the same as the expected system time of a customer requiring one unit of service (i.e., it is one unit of time plus the service time of all customers who arrive during that unit and during the service of other such customers). When one unit of service is completed for the given customer, the given customer is in service with one unit of service still required, which is the same as if a new customer arrived requiring one unit of service. Thus the given customer requiring 2 units of service has an expected system time of 2C. Extending the argument to a customer requiring n units of service, the expected system time is nC. Doing the argument backwards for a customer requiring 1/n of service, the expected system time is C/n. We thus conclude that E[system time | X=x] = Cx.

(d) We have

$$E[B] = \int_0^\infty Cx\, dF(x) = CE[X]; \quad C = \frac{1}{1 - \lambda E[X]}$$

3.50

(a) Since $\{p_j\}$ is the stationary distribution, we have for all $j \in S$

$$p_j\left(\sum_{i \in \bar{S}} q_{ji} + \sum_{i \notin \bar{S}} q_{ji}\right) = \sum_{i \in \bar{S}} p_i q_{ij} + \sum_{i \notin \bar{S}} p_i q_{ij}$$

Using the given relation, we obtain for all $j \in \bar{S}$

$$p_j \sum_{i \in \bar{S}} q_{ji} = \sum_{i \in \bar{S}} p_i q_{ij}$$

Dividing by $\sum_{i \in \bar{S}} p_i$, it follows that

$$\bar{p}_j \sum_{i \in \bar{S}} q_{ji} = \sum_{i \in \bar{S}} \bar{p}_i q_{ij}$$

for all $j \in \bar{S}$, showing that $\{\bar{p}_j\}$ is the stationary distribution of the truncated chain.

(b) If the original chain is time reversible, we have $p_j q_{ji} = p_i q_{ij}$ for all i and j, so the condition of part (a) holds. Therefore, we have $\bar{p}_j q_{ji} = \bar{p}_i q_{ij}$ for all states i and j of the truncated chain.

(c) The finite capacity system is a truncation of the two independent M/M/1 queues system, which is time reversible. Therefore, by part (b), the truncated chain is also time reversible. The formula for the steady state probabilities is a special case of Eq. (3.39) of Section 3.4.

3.51

(a) Since the detailed balance equations hold, we have

$$p_j q_{ji} = p_i q_{ij}$$

Thus for $i, j \in S_k$, we have

$$\frac{p_j}{u_k} q_{ji} = \frac{p_i}{u_k} q_{ij} \iff \pi_j q_{ji} = \pi_i q_{ij}$$

and it follows that the π_i, $i \in S_k$ satisfy the detailed balance equations. Also

$$\sum_{i \in S_k} \pi_i = \frac{\sum\limits_{i \in S_k} p_i}{u_k} = \frac{u_k}{u_k} = 1$$

Therefore, $\{\pi_i \mid i \in S_k\}$ as defined above, is the stationary distribution of the Markov chain with state space S_k.

(b) Obviously

$$\sum_{k=1}^{K} u_k = \sum_{k=1}^{K} \sum_{j \in S_k} p_j = 1. \tag{1}$$

Also we have

$$u_k \tilde{q}_{km} = \sum_{\substack{j \in S_k \\ i \in S_m}} \pi_j q_{ji} u_k,$$

which in view of the fact $\pi_j u_k = p_j$ for $j \in S_k$, implies that

$$u_k \tilde{q}_{km} = \sum_{\substack{j \in S_k \\ i \in S_m}} p_j q_{ji} \tag{2}$$

and

$$u_m \tilde{q}_{mk} = \sum_{\substack{j \in S_m \\ i \in S_k}} \pi_j q_{ji} u_m = \sum_{\substack{j \in S_m \\ i \in S_k}} q_{ji} p_j = \sum_{\substack{i \in S_m \\ j \in S_k}} q_{ij} p_j.$$

$$\tag{3}$$

Since the detailed balance equations $p_j q_{ji} = q_{ij} p_i$ hold, we have

$$\sum_{\substack{j \in S_k \\ i \in S_m}} p_j q_{ji} = \sum_{\substack{i \in S_m \\ j \in S_k}} q_{ij} p_i \tag{4}$$

Equations (2)-(4) give

$$u_k \tilde{q}_{km} = u_m \tilde{q}_{mk}. \tag{5}$$

Equations (1) and (5) imply that $\{u_k \mid k=1,...,K\}$ is the stationary distribution of the Markov chain with states $1,...,k$, and transition rates $\tilde{q}_{km}$.

(c) We will deal only with Example 3.13. (Example 3.12 is a special case with k=m).

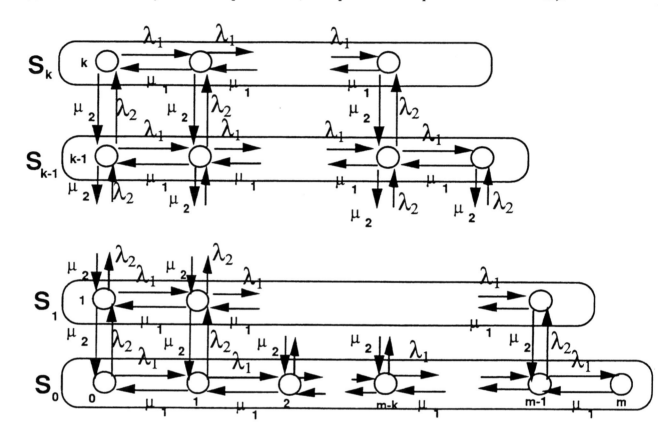

For $i = 0,1,...,k$ we define S_i as the set of states $(i,0), (i,1),..., (i,m-i)$, (see Figure 1). Then the truncated chain with state space S_i is

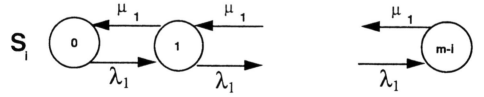

We denote by $\pi_j^{(i)}$ the stationary probability of state j of the truncated chain S_i and we let

$$\rho_1 = \frac{\lambda_1}{\mu_1}.$$

Then

$$\pi_{j+1}^{(i)} = \rho_1 \pi_j^{(i)}$$

Thus

$$\pi_0^{(i)} \sum_{j=0}^{m-i} \rho_1^{\,j} = 1.$$

or

$$\pi_0^{(i)} = \frac{1-p_1}{1-p_1^{m-i+1}}$$

Therefore,

$$\pi_j^{(i)} = \frac{1-\rho_1}{1-\rho_1^{m-i+1}}\,\rho_1^{\,j} \qquad i=0,1,2,...,k, \quad j=0,1,2,...,m-i$$

The transition probabilities of the aggregate chain are

$$\tilde{q}_{1,\,1+1} = \sum_{j\in S_1, i\in S_{1+1}} \pi_j^{(1)} q_{ji} = \sum_{j=0}^{m-1-1} \pi_j^{(1)}\lambda_2 = \lambda_2(1-\pi_{m-1}^{(1)})$$

$$= \lambda_2\left(1-\frac{1-\rho_1}{1-\rho_1^{m-1+1}}\,\rho_1^{m-1}\right) = \lambda_2\,\frac{1-\rho_1^{m-1}}{1-\rho_1^{m-1+1}}$$

$$\tilde{q}_{1+1,\,1} = \sum_{\substack{j\in S_{1+1} \\ i\in S_1}} \pi_j^{(1+1)} q_{ji} = \mu_2 \sum_{j\in S_{1+1}} \pi_j^{(1+1)} = \mu_2.$$

The aggregate chain is given by the following figure.

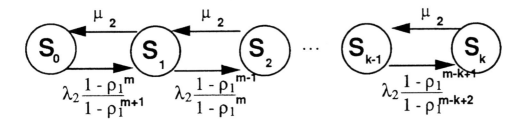

Thus we have

$$u_{1+1} = \rho_2 \cdot \frac{1-\rho_1^{m-1}}{1-\rho_1^{m-1+1}}\,u_1$$

from which

$$u_1 = \rho_2^{1} \, 2 \, \Pi_{j=0}^{1-1} \left(\frac{1-\rho_1^{m-j}}{1-\rho_1^{m-j+1}} \right) = \rho_2 \, \frac{1-\rho_1^{m-1+1}}{1-\rho_1^{m+1}} \, u_0$$

Furthermore, we have

$$\sum_{l=0}^{k} u_l = 1,$$

or

$$u_0 \sum_{l=0}^{k} \rho_2^{l} \, \frac{1-\rho_1^{m-1+1}}{1-\rho_1^{m+1}} = 1$$

from which

$$u_0 = \frac{1-\rho_1^{m+1}}{\dfrac{1-\rho_2^{k+1}}{1-\rho_2} - \rho_1^{m+1} \cdot \dfrac{1-\left(\dfrac{\rho_2}{\rho_1}\right)^{k+1}}{1-\dfrac{\rho_2}{\rho_1}}}$$

and

$$u_l = u_0 \, \rho_2^{l} \, \frac{1-\rho_1^{m-1+1}}{1-\rho_1^{m+1}}$$

Thus

$$p(n_1 n_2) = \pi_{n_1}^{(n_2)} u_{n_2} = \frac{u_0 \rho_2^{n_2}(1-\rho_1)\rho_1^{n_1}}{1-\rho_1^{m+1}}$$

from which we obtain the product form

$$p(n_1 n_2) = \left(\frac{1-\rho_2^{k+1}}{1-\rho_2} - \rho_1^{m+1} \, \frac{1-\left(\dfrac{\rho_2}{\rho_1}\right)^{k+1}}{1-\dfrac{\rho_2}{\rho_1}} \right)^{-1} (1-\rho_1) \, \rho_1^{n_1} \rho_2^{n_2}$$

(d) We are given that the detailed balance equations hold for the truncated chains. Thus for $i, j \in S_k$, we have $p_i q_{ij} = p_j q_{ji}$. Furthermore,

$$\sum_{i \in S_k} \pi_i = \sum_{i \in S_k} \frac{\rho_i}{u_k} = \frac{u_k}{u_k} = 1$$

Thus $\{\pi_j \mid j \in S_k\}$ is the distribution for the truncated chain S_k and the result of part (a) holds.

To prove the result of part (b), we have to prove that the global balance equations hold for the aggregate chain, i.e.,

$$\sum_{m=1}^{k} \tilde{q}_{km} u_k = \sum_{m=1}^{k} u_m \tilde{q}_{mk},$$

or equivalently

$$\sum_{m=1}^{k} \sum_{j \in S_k, i \in S_m} \pi_j u_k q_{ji} = \sum_{m=1}^{k} \sum_{j \in S_k, i \in S_m} q_{ij} \pi_i u_m$$

For $j \in S_k$, we have $\pi_j u_k = p_j$, and for $i \in S_m$, we have $\pi_i u_m = p_i$, so we must show

$$\sum_{m=1}^{k} \sum_{j \in S_k, i \in S_m} p_j q_{ji} = \sum_{m=1}^{k} \sum_{j \in S_k, i \in S_m} q_{ij} p_i$$

or

$$\sum_{j \in S_k} \sum_{\text{all } i} p_j q_{ji} = \sum_{j \in S_k} \sum_{\text{all } i} p_i q_{ij} \tag{6}$$

Since $\{p_i\}$ is the distribution of the original chain, the global balance equations

$$\sum_{\text{all } i} p_j q_{ji} = \sum_{\text{all } i} p_i q_{ij}$$

By summing over all $j \in S_k$, we see that Eq. (6) holds. Since

$$\sum_{k=1}^{} u_k = 1$$

and we just proved that the u_k's satisfy the global balance equations for the aggregate chain, $\{u_k \mid k = 1,...,K\}$ is the distribution of the aggregate chain. This proves the result of part (b).

3.52

Consider a customer arriving at time t_1 and departing at time t_2. In reversed system terms, the arrival process is independent Poisson, so the arrival process to the left of t_2 is independent of the times spent in the system of customers that arrived at or to the right of t_2. In particular, $t_2 - t_1$ is independent of the (reversed system) arrival process to the left of t_2. In forward system terms, this means that $t_2 - t_1$ is independent of the departure process to the left of t_2.

3.53

(a) If customers are served in the order they arrive then given that a customer departs at time t from queue 1, the arrival time of that customer at queue 1 (and therefore the time spent at queue 1), is independent of the departure process from queue 1 prior to t. Since the departures from queue 1 are arrivals at queue 2, we conclude that the time spent by a customer at queue 1 is independent of the arrival times at queue 2 prior to the customer's arrival at queue2. These arrival times, together with the corresponding independent (by Kleinrock's approximation) service times determine the time the customer spends at queue 2 and the departure process from queue 2 before the customer's departure from queue 2.

(b) Suppose packets with mean service time $1/\mu$ arrive at the tandem queues with some rate λ which is very small ($\lambda \ll \mu$). Then, the apriori probability that a packet will wait in queue 2 is very small.

Assume now that we know that the waiting time of a packet in queue 1 was nonzero. This information changes the aposteriori probability that the packet will wait in queue 2 to at least 1/2 (because its service time in queue 1 will be less than the service time at queue 2 of the packet in front of it with probability 1/2). Thus the knowledge that the waiting time in queue 1 is nonzero, provides a lot of information about the waiting time in queue 2.

3.54

The Markov chain for an M/M/1/m system is

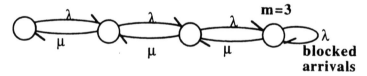

Since this is a birth/death process, the chain is reversible. If we include the arrivals that are blocked from the system, then the arrival process is Poisson (by definition of M/M/1/m). If we include the blocked arrivals also as departures, then the departure process is also Poisson (by reversibility).

Blocked arrivals and departing blocked arrivals

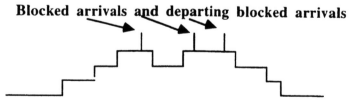

If we omit the blocked arrivals from consideration, the admitted arrival process has rate $\lambda(1-P_m)$, but this process is definitely not Poisson. One could, if one were truly masochistic, calculate things like the interarrival density, but the only sensible way to characterize the process is to characterize it jointly with the state process, in which case it is simply the process of arrivals during intervals when the state is less than m. The departure process, omitting the departures of blocked arrivals, is the same as the process of admitted arrivals, as can be seen by reversibility.

3.55

Let

$$\rho_1 = \frac{\lambda_1}{\mu_1}$$

$$\rho_2 = \frac{\lambda_2}{\mu_2}$$

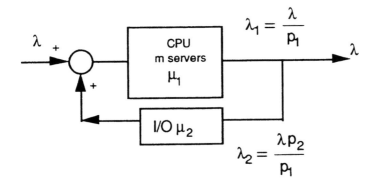

Using Jackson's Theorem and Eqs. (3.34)-(3.35) we find that

$$P(n_1, n_2) = \begin{cases} P_0 \dfrac{(m\rho_1)^{n_1}}{n_1!} \cdot \rho_2^{n_2}(1-\rho_2), & n_1 \le m \\[2ex] P_0 \dfrac{m^m \rho_1^{n_1}}{m!} \rho_2^{n_2}(1-\rho_2), & n_1 > m \end{cases}$$

where

$$P_0 = \left[\sum_{n=0}^{m-1} \frac{(m\rho_1)^n}{n!} + \frac{(m\rho_1)^m}{m!(1-\rho_1)} \right]^{-1}$$

3.56

(a) We have

$$P(X_n=i) = (1-\rho)\rho^i; \quad i \ge 0; \quad \rho = \lambda/\mu$$

$$P(X_n=i, D_n=j) = P(D_n=j \mid X_n=i) P(X_n=i) = \mu\Delta(1-\rho)\rho^i; \quad i \ge 1, j=1$$
$$= 0; \quad i=0, j=1$$
$$= (1-\mu\Delta)(1-\rho)\rho^i; \quad i \ge 1, j=0$$
$$= 1-\rho; \quad i=0, j=0$$

(b) $P(D_n=1) = \sum_{i=1} \mu\Delta((1-\rho)\rho^i = \mu\Delta\rho = \lambda\Delta$

(c) $P(X_n=i \mid D_n=1) = \dfrac{P(X_n=i, D_n=1)}{P(D_n=1)} = \{\mu\Delta(1-\rho)\rho^i\}/\lambda\Delta = (1-\rho)\rho^{i-1}; \quad i \ge 1$
$$= 0; \quad i=0$$

(d) $P(X_{n+1}=i|\ D_n=1) = P(X_n=i+1|\ D_n=1) = (1-\rho)\rho^i$; $i \geq 0$

In the first equality above, we use the fact that, given a departure between $n\Delta$ and $(n+1)\Delta$, the state at $(n+1)\Delta$ is one less than the state at $n\Delta$; in the second equality, we use part d). Since $P(X_{n+1}=i) = (1-\rho)\rho^i$, we see that X_{n+1} is statistically independent of the event $D_n=1$. It is thus also independent of the complementary event $D_n=0$, and thus is independent of the random variable D_n.

(e) $P(X_{n+1}=i, D_{n+1}=j\ |\ D_n) = P(D_{n+1}=j\ |\ X_{n+1}=i, D_n)P(X_{n+1}=i\ |\ D_n)$

$$= P(D_{n+1}=j\ |\ X_{n+1}=i)P(X_{n+1}=i\ )$$

The first part of the above equality follows because X_{n+1} is the state of the Markov process at time $(n+1)\Delta$, so that, conditional on that state, D_{n+1} is independent of everything in the past. The second part of the equality follows from the independence established in e). This establishes that X_{n+1}, D_{n+1} are independent of D_n; thus their joint distribution is given by b).

(f) We assume the inductive result for k-1 and prove it for k; note that part f establishes the result for k=1. Using the hint,

$P(X_{n+k}=i|\ D_{n+k-1}=1, D_{n+k-2},..., D_n) = P(X_{n+k-1}=i+1|\ D_{n+k-1}=1,D_{n+k-2},..., D_n)$

$$= \frac{P(X_{n+k-1}=i+1, D_{n+k-1}=1|D_{n+k-2},..., D_n)}{P(D_{n+k-1}=1|\ D_{n+k-2},..., D_n)}$$

$$= \frac{P(X_{n+k-1}=i+1,D_{n+k-1}=1)}{P(D_{n+k-1}=1)}$$

$$= P(X_{n+k-1}=i+1|\ D_{n+k-1}=1) = P(X_{n+k}=i\ |\ D_{n+k-1}=1)$$

The third equality above used the inductive hypothesis for the independence of the pair (X_{n+k-1},D_{n+k-1}) from $D_{n+k-2},...D_n$ in the numerator and the corresponding independence of D_{n+k-1} in the denominator. From part e), with n+k-1 replacing n, $P(X_{n+k}=i\ |\ D_{n+k-1}) = P(X_{n+k}=i)$, so

$$P(X_{n+k}=i|\ D_{n+k-1}=1, D_{n+k-2},..., D_n) = P(X_{n+k})$$

Using the argument in e), this shows that conditional on $D_{n+k-2},..., D_n$, the variable X_{n+k} is independent of the event $D_{n+k-1}=1$ and thus also independent of $D_{n+k-1}=0$. Thus X_{n+k} is independent of $D_{n+k-1},..., D_n$. Finally,

$$P(X_{n+k}=i, D_{n+k}=j\ |\ D_{n+k-1},..., D_n) = P(D_{n+k}=j\ |\ X_{n+k}=i)P(X_{n+k}=i|\ D_{n+k-1},..., D_n)$$

$$= P(D_{n+k}=j\ |\ X_{n+k}=i)P(X_{n+k}=i)$$

which shows the desired independence for k.

(g) This shows that the departure process is Bernoulli and that the state is independent of past departures; i.e., we have proved the first two parts of Burke's theorem without using reversibility. What is curious here is that the state independence is critical in establishing the Bernoulli property.

3.57

The session numbers and their rates are shown below:

Session	Session number p	Session rate x_p
ACE	1	$100/60 = 5/3$
ADE	2	$200/60 = 10/3$
BCEF	3	$500/60 = 25/3$
BDEF	4	$600/60 = 30/3$

The link numbers and the total link rates calculated as the sum of the rates of the sessions crossing the links are shown below:

Link	Total link rate
AC	$x_1 = 5/3$
CE	$x_1 + x_3 = 30/3$
AD	$x_2 = 10/3$
BD	$x_4 = 10$
DE	$x_2 + x_4 = 40/3$
BC	$x_3 = 25/3$
EF	$x_3 + x_4 = 55/3$

For each link (i,j) the service rate is

$$\mu_{ij} = 50000/1000 = 50 \text{ packets/sec,}$$

and the propagation delay is $D_{ij} = 2 \times 10^{-3}$ secs. The total arrival rate to the system is

$$\gamma = \Sigma_i x_i = 5/3 + 10/3 + 25/3 + 30/3 = 70/3$$

The average number on each link (i, j) (based on the Kleinrock approximation formula) is:

$$N_{ij} = \frac{\lambda_{ij}}{\mu_{ij} - \lambda_{ij}} + \lambda_{ij} D_{ij}$$

From this we obtain:

Link	Average Number of Packets on the Link
AC	$(5/3)/(150/3 - 5/3) + (5/3)(2/1000) = 5/145 + 1/300$
CE	$1/4 + 1/50$
AD	$1/14 + 1/150$
BD	$1/4 + 1/50$

DE	4/11 + 2/75
BC	1/5 + 1/60
EF	11/19 + 11/300

The average total number in the system is $N = \Sigma_{(i,j)} N_{ij} \cong 1.84$ packet. The average delay over all sessions is $T = N/\gamma = 1.84 \times (3/70) = 0.0789$ secs. The average delay of the packets of an individual session are obtained from the formula

$$T_p = \sum_{(i,j) \text{ on } p} \left[\frac{\lambda_{ij}}{\mu_{ij}(\mu_{ij} - \lambda_{ij})} + \frac{1}{\mu_{ij}} + D_{ij} \right]$$

For the given sessions we obtain applying this formula

Session p	Average Delay T_p
1	0.050
2	0.053
3	0.087
4	0.090

3.58

We convert the system into a closed network with M customers as indicated in the hint. The (k+1)st queue corresponds to the "outside world". It is easy to see that the queues of the open systems are equivalent to the first k queues of the closed system. For example, when there is at least one customer in the (k+1)st queue (equivalently, there are less than M customers in the open system) the arrival rate at queue i is

$$\sum_{m=1}^{k} r_m \frac{r_i}{\sum_{j=1}^{k} r_j} = r_i .$$

Furthermore, when the (k+1)st queue is empty no external arrivals can occur at any queue i, i = 1,2,...,k. If we denote with $p(n_1,...,n_k)$ the steady state distribution for the open system, we get

$$p(n_1,n_2,...,n_k) = \begin{cases} 0 & \text{if } \sum_{i=1}^{k} n_i > M \\ \\ \dfrac{\rho_1^{n_1} \rho_2^{n_2} \cdots \rho_k^{n_k} \rho_{k+1}^{\left(M - \sum_{i=1}^{k} n_i\right)}}{G(M)} & \text{otherwise} \end{cases}$$

where

$$\rho_i = \frac{r_i}{\mu}, \ i = 1, 2, \ldots, k,$$

$$\rho_{k+1} = \frac{\sum_{i=1}^{k} r_i (1 - \sum_{j=1}^{k} p_{ij})}{\sum_{i=1}^{k} r_i}$$

and $G(M)$ is the normalizing factor.

3.59

If we insert a very fast M/M/1 queue ($\mu \to \infty$) between a pair of queues, then the probability distribution for the packets in the rest of the queues is not affected. If we condition on a single customer being in the fast queue, since this customer will remain in this queue for $1/\mu$ ($\to 0$) time on the average, it is equivalent to conditioning on a customer moving from one queue to the other in the original system.

If $P(n_1, \ldots, n_k)$ is the stationary distribution of the original system of k queues and $P'(n_1, \ldots, n_k, n_{k+1})$ is the corresponding probability distribution after the insertion of the fast queue k+1, then

$$P(n_1, \ldots, n_k \mid arrival) = P'(n_1, \ldots, n_k, \ n_{k+1} = 1 \mid n_{k+1} = 1),$$

which by independence of $n_1, \ldots, n_k, n_{k+1},$ is equal to $P(n_1, \ldots, n_k)$.

3.60

Let U_j = utility function of jth queue.

We have to prove that

$$\lim_{M \to \infty}(U_j(M)) = \lim_{M \to \infty} \frac{\lambda_j(M)}{\mu_j} = 1$$

But from problem 3.65 we have

$$U_j(M) = \rho_j \frac{G(M-1)}{G(M)}.$$

Thus it is enough to prove that

$$\lim_{M \to \infty} \frac{G(M)}{G(M-1)} = \rho_j$$

where $\rho_j = \max\{\rho_1,..., \rho_k\}$. We have

$$G(M) = \sum_{n_1+...+n_k = M} \rho_1^{n_1}...\rho_j^{n_j}...\rho_k^{n_k} = \sum_{\substack{n_1+...+n_k = M \\ n_j = 0}} \rho_1^{n_1}...\rho_j^{n_j}...\rho_k^{n_k} + \sum_{\substack{n_1+...+n_k = M \\ n_j \neq 0}} \rho_1^{n_1}...\rho_j^{n_j}...\rho_k^{n_k}$$

$$= A(M) + B(M) \tag{1}$$

Since $\rho_j = \max\{\rho_1,...,\rho_k\}$ we have that

$$\lim_{M \to \infty} \frac{A(M)}{B(M)} = 0.$$

Thus, Eq. (1) implies that

$$\lim_{M \to \infty} \frac{\sum_{\substack{n_1+...+n_k = M \\ n_j \neq 0}} \rho_1^{n_1}...\rho_j^{n_j}...\rho_k^{u_k}}{G(M)} = 1$$

or, denoting $n'_j = n_j - 1$,

$$\lim_{M \to \infty} \frac{\rho_j \sum_{n_1+...+n'_j+...+n_k = M-1} \rho_1^{n_1}...\rho_j^{n'_j}...\rho_k^{n_k}}{G(M)} = 1$$

or

$$\lim_{M \to \infty} \frac{\rho_j G(M-1)}{G(M)} = 1$$

3.61

We have $\sum_{i=0}^{m} p_i = 1$.

The arrival rate at the CPU is λ/p_0 and the arrival rate at the ith I/O port is $\lambda p_i/p_0$. By Jackson's Theorem, we have

$$P(n_0, n_1, \ldots, n_m) = \prod_{i=o}^{m} \rho_i^{n_i} (1 - \rho_i)$$

where $\rho = \dfrac{\lambda}{\mu_0\, p_0}$

and $\rho_i = \dfrac{\lambda\, p_i}{\mu_i\, p_0}$ for $i > 0$

The equivalent tandem system is as follows:

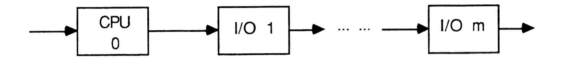

The arrival rate is λ. The service rate for queue 0 is $\mu_0 p_0$ and for queue i (i > 0) is $\mu_i p_0/p_i$.

3.62

Let λ_0 be the arrival rate at the CPU and let λ_i be the arrival rate at I/O unit i. We have

$$\lambda_i = p_i \lambda_0, \quad i = 1,\ldots,m.$$

Let

$$\overline{\lambda}_0 = 1, \quad \overline{\lambda}_i = p_i, \quad i = 1,\ldots,m,$$

and

$$\rho_i = \frac{\overline{\lambda}_i}{\mu_i}, \quad i = 0,1,\ldots,m,$$

By Jackson's Theorem, the occupancy distribution is

$$P(n_0, n_1,\ldots,n_m) = \frac{\rho_0^{n_0} \rho_1^{n_1} \cdots \rho_m^{n_m}}{G(M)},$$

where G(M) is the normalization constant corresponding to M customers,

$$G(M) = \sum_{n_0 + n_1 + \cdots + n_m = M} \rho_0^{n_0} \rho_1^{n_1} \cdots \rho_m^{n_m}$$

Let

$$U_0 = \frac{\lambda_0}{\mu_0}$$

be the utilization factor of the CPU. We have

$$U_0 = P(n_0 \geq 1) = \sum_{\substack{n_0+n_1+\ldots+n_m=M \\ n_0 \geq 1}} P(n_0,n_1,\ldots,n_m)$$

$$= \sum_{n'_0+n_1+\ldots+n_m=M-1} \frac{\rho_0^{n'_0+1},\rho_1^{n_1}\cdots\rho_m^{n_m}}{G(M)}$$

$$= \rho_0 \frac{G(M-1)}{G(M)} = \frac{1}{\mu_0}\frac{G(M-1)}{G(M)},$$

where we used the change of variables $n'_0 = n_0-1$. Thus the arrival rate at the CPU is

$$\lambda_0 = \frac{G(M-1)}{G(M)}$$

and the arrival rate at the I/O unit i is

$$\lambda_i = \frac{p_i G(M-1)}{G(M)}, \quad i=1,\ldots,m.$$

3.63

(a) We have $\lambda = N/T$ and

$$T = T_1 + T_2 + T_3$$

where

T_1 = Average time at first transmission line
T_2 = Average time at second transmission line
$T_3 = \overline{Z}$

We have

$$\overline{X} \leq T_1 \leq N\overline{X} \tag{1}$$

$$\overline{Y} \leq T_2 \leq N\overline{Y}$$

so

$$\frac{N}{N(\overline{X}+\overline{Y})+\overline{Z}}\le\lambda\le\frac{N}{\overline{X}+\overline{Y}+\overline{Z}}\ .$$

Also

$$\lambda\le\frac{K}{\overline{X}},\qquad\lambda\le\frac{1}{\overline{Y}}$$

so finally

$$\frac{N}{N(\overline{X}+\overline{Y})+\overline{Z}}\le\lambda\le\min\left\{\frac{K}{\overline{X}},\frac{1}{\overline{Y}},\frac{N}{\overline{X}+\overline{Y}+\overline{Z}}\right\}$$

(b) The same line of argument applies except that in place of (1) we have

$$\overline{X}\le T_1\le (N-K+1)\overline{X}$$

3.64

(a) The state is determined by the number of customers at node 1 (one could use node 2 just as easily). When there are customers at node 1 (which is the case for states 1, 2, and 3), the departure rate from node 1 is μ_1; each such departure causes the state to decrease as shown below. When there are customers in node 2 (which is the case for states 0, 1, and 2), the departure rate from node 2 is μ_2; each such departure causes the state to increase.

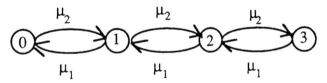

(b) Letting p_i be the steady state probability of state i, we have $p_i = p_{i-1}\,\rho$, where $\rho = \mu_2/\mu_1$. Thus $p_i = p_0\rho^i$. Solving for p_0,

$$p_0 = [1+\rho+\rho^2+\rho^3]^{-1},\qquad p_i = p_0\,\rho^i;\quad i=1,2,3.$$

(c) Customers leave node 1 at rate μ_1 for all states other than state 0. Thus the time average rate r at which customers leave node 1 is $\mu_1(1-P_0)$, which is

$$r=\frac{\rho+\rho^2+\rho^3}{1+\rho+\rho^2+\rho^3}\,\mu_1$$

(d) Since there are three customers in the system, each customer cycles at one third the rate at which departures occur from node 1. Thus a customer cycles at rate r/3.

(e) The Markov process is a birth-death process and thus reversible. What appears as a departure from node i in the forward process appears as an arrival to node i in the backward process. If we order the customers 1, 2, and 3 in the order in which they depart a node, and note that this order never changes (because of the FCFS service at each node), then we see that in the backward process, the customers keep their identity, but the order is reversed with backward departures from node i in the order 3, 2, 1, 3, 2, 1, ...

3.65

Since $\mu_j(m) = \mu_j$ for all m, and the probability distribution for state $n = (n_1,...,n_k)$ is

$$P(n) = \frac{\rho_1^{n_1}...\rho_k^{n_k}}{G(M)},$$

where

$$\rho_j = \frac{\overline{\lambda}_j}{\mu_j}$$

The utilization factor $U_j(M)$ for queue j is

$$U_j(M) = \sum_{\substack{n_1+...+n_k=M \\ s.t.\, n_j \neq 0}} P(n) = \frac{\sum_{\substack{n_1+...+n_k=M \\ n_j \neq 0}} \rho_1^{n_1}...\rho_k^{n_k}}{G(M)},$$

Denoting $n'_j = n_j-1$, we get

$$U_j(M) = \frac{\sum_{n_1+...+n'_j...+n_k=M-1} \rho_1^{n_1}...\rho_j^{n'_j}...\rho_k^{n_k} \cdot \rho_j}{G(M)} = \frac{\rho_j G(M-1)}{G(M)}.$$

3.66

Let c_i indicate the class of the ith customer in queue.

We consider a state $(c_1,c_2,...,c_n)$ such that $\mu_{c_1} \neq \mu_{c_n}$.

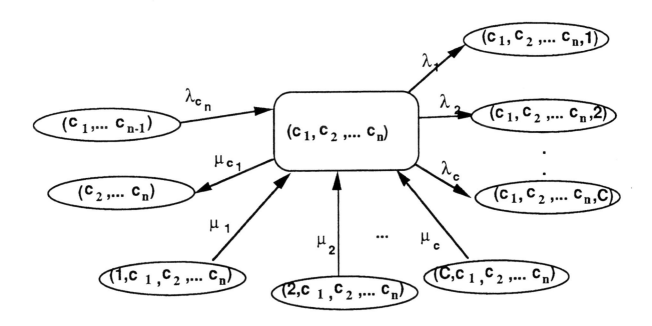

If the steady-state distribution has a product form then the global balance equations for this state give

$$p(c_1)\cdots p(c_n)(\mu_{c_1} + \lambda_1 + \cdots + \lambda_c) = p(c_1)\cdots p(c_{n-1})\lambda_{c_n}$$
$$+ (\mu_1 p(1) + \mu_2 p(2) + \cdots + \mu_c p(c))\, p(c_1)\cdot\ldots\cdot p(c_n)$$

or

$$p(c_n)(\mu_{c_1} + \lambda_1 + \cdots + \lambda_c) = \lambda_{c_n} + (\mu_1 p(1) + \mu_2 p(2) + \cdots + \mu_c p(c))\cdot p(c_n)$$

Denote

$$M = \mu_1 p(1) + \mu_2 p(2) + \cdots + \mu_c p(c)$$

$$\lambda = \lambda_1 + \cdots + \lambda_c.$$

Then

$$p(c_n)(\mu_{c_1} + \lambda) = \lambda_{c_n} + M \cdot p(c_n)$$

or

$$p(c_n) = \frac{\lambda_{c_n}}{\mu_{c_1} + \lambda - M}$$

This is a contradiction because even if $\lambda_{c_1} = 0$, $p(c_n)$ still depends on μ_{c_1}. The contradiction gives that $\mu_{c_1} = \mu$ = constant for every class. Thus we can model this system by a Markov chain only if $\mu_1 = \mu_2 = \cdots = \mu_c$.

(b) We will prove that the detailed balance equations hold. Based on the following figure

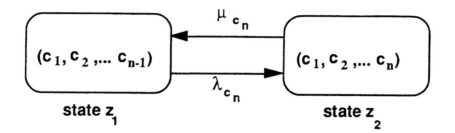

the detailed balance equations are

$$\lambda_{c_n} \cdot p(z_1) = \mu_{c_n} \cdot p(z_2)$$

or

$$\lambda_{c_n} p_{c_1} \cdots p_{c_{n-1}} = \mu_{c_n} p_{c_1} \cdots p_{c_n},$$

which obviously holds.

CHAPTER 4 SOLUTIONS

4.1

a) State n can only be reached from states 0 to n+1, so, using Eq. (3A.1),

$$p_n = \sum_{i=0}^{n+1} p_i P_{in} \;\; ; \quad 0 \le n < m$$

$$\sum_{n=0}^{m} p_n = 1$$

b) Solving for the final term, p_{n+1}, in the first sum above,

$$p_{n+1} = \frac{p_n(1-P_{nn}) - \displaystyle\sum_{i=0}^{n-1} p_i P_{in}}{P_{n+1,n}}$$

c) $\quad p_1 = p_0(1-P_{00})/P_{10}$

$$p_2 = \frac{p_1(1-P_{11})-p_0 P_{02}}{P_{21}} = p_0\left[\frac{(1-P_{00})(1-P_{11})}{P_{10}P_{21}} - \frac{P_{02}}{P_{21}} \right]$$

d) Combining the above equations with $p_0+p_1+p_2 = 1$, we get

$$p_0 = \frac{P_{10}P_{21}}{P_{10}P_{21}+(1-P_{00})P_{21}+(1-P_{00})(1-P_{11})-P_{02}P_{10}}$$

4.2

a) $\quad P_{succ} = Q_a(1,n)Q_r(0,n) + Q_a(0,n)Q_r(1,n)$

Using Eqs(4.1) and (4.2),

$$P_{succ} = [(m-n)(1-q_a)^{m-n-1}q_a](1-q_r)^n + (1-q_a)^{m-n}[n(1-q_r)^{n-1}q_r]$$

$$= (1-q_a)^{m-n}(1-q_r)^n\left[(m-n)\frac{q_a}{1-q_a} + n\frac{q_r}{1-q_r} \right]$$

b) Approximate $q_a/(1-q_a)$ by q_a in the bracketed espression above. This is a good approximation for q_a small, whereas we cannot similarly approximate $(1-q_a)^{m-n}$ by 1 since m-n might be large. We also approximate $q_r/(1-q_r)$ by q_r. Using the approximation $(1-x)^y \approx e^{-xy}$, we then get

$$P_{succ} \approx \exp[-(m-n)q_a - nq_r] \{(m-n)q_a + nq_r\} = G(n)e^{-G(n)}$$

c) $(1-x)^y = \exp[y \ln(1-x)] = \exp[y (-x - x^2/2 - x^3/3 \,...)]$

$$= \exp(-yx) \exp[-x^2 y/2 - x^3 y/3 \,...]$$

which is equivalent to the desired relation. Note that for the approximation to be close (in terms of percentage error), $x^2 y$ must be close to 0.

4.3

a)

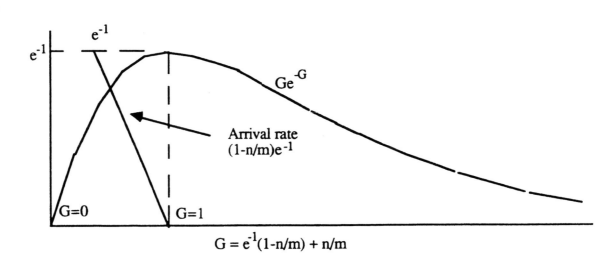

$$G = e^{-1}(1-n/m) + n/m$$

b) $P_{succ} = m q_r (1-q_r)^{m-1} \approx 1/e$

where we have used $m q_r = 1$ and the result of problem 4.2.

c) Note that a straight line from (mq_a, mq_a) to the point $(1, 0)$ can only cross the curve Ge^{-G} once. For $mq_a \leq 1$ this crossing corresponds to a stable point by the argument in fig. 4.4. For $mq_a > 1$, we have $q_a > q_r$; when the departure rate exceeds the arrival rate, then n tends to decrease, which corresponds to motion toward the right on the figure. Thus the crossing corresponds to a stable point in this case also.

d) The stable point occurs at the intersection of the curve and straight line above, i.e. where

$$Ge^{-G} = (1-G)/(e-1)$$

Solving numerically, $G = 0.4862$.

e) Solving for n/m from G, we have $n/m = (eG-1)/(e-1) = 0.1872$. Thus at equilibrium a rather large fraction of the arriving packets (i.e., 0.1872) are not accepted by the system.

4.4

a) Let $E\{n\}$ be the expected number of backlogged nodes, averaged over time. Since $m-E\{n\}$ is the expected number of nodes that can accept packets, and q_a is the probability that each receives a packet in a slot, the expected number of accepted arrivals per slot is

$$E\{N_a\} = q_a(m-E\{n\})$$

b) Since a limited number (i.e., m) arrivals can be in the system at any time, the time average accepted arrival rate must equal the time average departure rate, which is the time average success rate, $E\{P_{succ}\}$. Thus

$$E\{P_{succ}\} = E\{N_a\} = q_a(m-E\{n\})$$

c) The expected number of packets in the system, $E\{N_{sys}\}$ immediately after the beginning of a slot is the expected backlog, $E\{n\}$, plus the expected number of arrivals accepted during the previous slot, $E\{N_a\}$. Thus,

$$E\{N_{sys}\} = E\{n\} + E\{N_a\} = E\{n\}(1-q_a) + q_a m$$

d) From Little's theorem, the expected delay T is $E\{N_{sys}\}$ divided by the accepted arrival rate $E\{N_a\}\}$ Note that we are only counting the delay of the packets accepted into the system and note also that we are regarding accepted arrivals as arriving discretely at the slot boundaries.

$$T = E\{N_{sys}\}/E\{N_a\} = 1 + E\{n\}/[q_a(m-E\{n\})]$$

e) The above equations express the relevant quantities in terms of $E\{n\}$ and make clear that $E\{N_a\}$ and $E\{P_{succ}\}$ decrease and $E\{N_{sys}\}$ and T increase as n is decreased. Thus it makes no difference which of these quantities is optimized; improving one improves the others.

4.5

a) The probability that a packet is successful on the first slot is p, and given that it has not been successful before the ith slot, the probability that it is successful there is pq_r, i.e., the probability of retransmission times the probability of success. Thus the unconditioned probability of success on the second slot is $(1-p)pq_r$. Similarly, the probability of success on the third slot is $(1-p)(1-pq_r)pq_r$, and in general on the ith slot, i>2, is $(1-p)(1-pq_r)^{i-2}pq_r$. Thus, multiplying each term above by i and summing,

$$T = p + \sum_{i=2}^{\infty}(1-p)(1-pq_r)^{i-2}pq_r = 1 + \frac{1-p}{pq_r}$$

The solution to problem 2.17 b shows how to sum the above series.

b) The probability that a given packet transmission is successful is the probability that no other packets are transmitted in the same slot. If the given transmitted packet is a backlogged packet, then

$$p = (1-q_a)^{m-n}(1-q_r)^{n-1}$$

Approximating $(1-x)^k$ by e^{-kx} and approximating $(1-x)^{k-1}$ also by e^{-kx}, we get

$$p \approx e^{-G(n)} ; \quad G(n) = (m-n)q_a + nq_r$$

If the given transmitted packet is a new arrival, then p changes to $(1-q_a)^{m-n-1}(1-q_r)^n$, but the final result with the above approximation is the same. See the solution to problem 4.2 for a more complete discussion of these approximations.

c) Letting $G = G(n^*)$ and substituting e^{-G} for p in the solution to a),

$$T = 1 + (1-e^{-G})/(q_r e^{-G}) = 1 + (e^G - 1)/q_r$$

Since $G = (m-n^*)q_a + n^* q_r$ and $Ge^{-G} = (m-n^*)q_a$, the ratio of these equations yields

$$e^G = 1 + \frac{n^* q_r}{(m-n^*)q_a}$$

$$T = 1 + \frac{n^*}{(m-n^*)q_a}$$

d) The two equations above relating G and n^* can be solved simultaneously (numerically) to yield $n^*/m = 0.124... \approx 1/8$. Using this in the equation for T above yields $1 + 0.472m$. Thus, $T \approx m/2$. We can compare this with TDM in two ways. First, if only one packet can be saved at a node, then a fraction $1-e^{-0.3} = 0.259...$ of the slots carry packets, so a fraction 0.136 of the arriving packets are discarded and the delay is roughly $m/2$ (slightly larger if the latest arrival for a node is discarded when a packet is already there, and slightly less if the later arrival is kept and the earlier thrown away). Alternatively, if no packets are thrown away, then the delay (from Eq. (3.58)) is $m/1.4$. Whichever way one looks at it, slotted Aloha does not look attractive from a delay standpoint if one achieves stability by choosing $q_r m = 1$.

4.6

a) Substituting Eqs. (4.1) and (4.2) into (4.5),

$$P_{succ} = (m-n)q_a(1-q_a)^{m-n-1}(1-q_r)^n + nq_r(1-q_a)^{m-n}(1-q_r)^{n-1}$$

Differentiating this with respect to q_r (for $n > 1$) and consolidating terms, we get

$$\frac{\partial P_{succ}}{\partial q_r} = n(1-q_a)^{m-n}(1-q_r)^{n-1}\left[\frac{1}{1-q_r} - \frac{q_a(m-n)}{1-q_a} - \frac{q_r n}{1-q_r}\right]$$

The quantity inside brackets is decreasing in q_r; it is positive for $q_r = 0$ and negative as q_r approaches 1. Thus there is a point at which this quantity is 0 and that point maximizes P_{succ}.

b) If we set q_r equal to q_a in the bracketed quantity above, it becomes $(1-q_a m)/(1-q_r)$. This is positive under the assumption that $q_a < 1/m$. Thus, since the quantity in brackets is decreasing in q_r, it is zero for $q_r > q_a$.

c)
$$\frac{dP_{succ}}{dq_a} = \frac{\partial P_{succ}}{\partial q_a} + \frac{dq_r(q_a)}{dq_a}\frac{\partial P_{succ}}{\partial q_r} = \frac{\partial P_{succ}}{\partial q_a}$$

The above relation follows because $\partial P_{succ}/\partial q_r = 0$ at $q_r(q_a)$. We then have

$$\frac{\partial P_{succ}}{\partial q_a} = n(1-q_a)^{m-n-1}(1-q_r)^n\left[\frac{1}{1-q_a} - \frac{q_a(m-n)}{1-q_a} - \frac{q_r n}{1-q_r}\right]$$

Note that the bracketed term here differs from the bracketed term in part a) only in the first term. Since the bracketed term in part a) is 0 at $q_r(q_a)$ and $q_r(q_a) > q_a$, it follows that the bracketed term here is negative. Thus the total derivative of P_{succ} with respect to q_a is negative.

d) If arrivals are immediately regarded as backlogged, then an unbacklogged node generates a transmission with probability $q_a q_r$. Thus the probability of success is modified by replacing q_a with $q_a q_r$. This reduces the value of q_a in P_{succ} and therefore, from part c), increases the value of P_{succ} at the optimum choice of q_r.

4.7

a) Note that one packet successfully leaves the system each slot in which one or more packets are transmitted. Thus if all waiting packets attempt transmission in every slot, a successful transmission occurs in every slot in which packets are waiting. Since the expected delay is independent of the order in which packets are successfully transmitted (since each packet requires one slot), we see that the expected delay is the same as that of a centralized slotted FCFS system. Now compare this policy with an arbitrary policy for transmitting waiting packets; assume any given sequence of packet arrival times. Each time the arbitrary policy fails to attempt a transmission in a slot with waiting packets, the FCFS system (if it has waiting packets) decreases the backlog by 1 while the other policy does not decrease the backlog. Thus the backlog for the arbitrary system is always greater than or equal to that of the FCFS system (a formal proof of this would follow by induction on successive slots). Thus, by Little's relation, the arbitrary system has an expected delay at least as great as the FCFS system.

b) This is just the slotted FDM system of section 3.5.1 with m=1 (i.e., a slotted M/D/1 queueing system). From Eq. (3.58), the queueing delay is $1/[2(1-\lambda)]$ slot times. The total delay, including service time, is then $1 + 1/[2(1-\lambda)]$.

c) The solution to b) can be rewritten as $1 + 1/2 + \lambda/[2(1-\lambda)]$ where the first term is the transmission time (i.e., 1 slot), the second term is the waiting time from an arrival to the beginning of a slot, and the third term is the delay due to collisions with other packets. If each subsequent attempt after an unsuccessful attempt is delayed by k slots, this last term is multiplied by k. Thus the new total delay is $3/2 + k\lambda/[(1-\lambda)]$.

4.8

a) Let X be the time in slots from the beginning of a backlogged slot until the completion of the first success at a given node. Let $q = q_r p$ and note that q is the probability that the node will be successful at any given slot given that it is still backlogged. Thus

$$P\{X=i\} = q(1-q)^{i-1}\ ;\ i \geq 1$$

$$E\{X\} = \sum_{i=1}^{\infty} iq(1-q)^{i-1} = \frac{1}{q}$$

The above summation uses the identity

$$\sum_{i=1}^{\infty} i z^{i-1} = \sum_{i=1}^{\infty} \frac{dz^i}{dz} = \frac{d\sum_{i}^{\infty} z^i}{dz} = \frac{d[z/(1-z)]}{dz} = \frac{1}{(1-z)^2}$$

Taking $q = 1-z$ gives the desired result. A similar identity needed for the second moment is

$$\sum_{i=1}^{\infty} i^2 z^{i-1} = \sum_{i=1}^{\infty} \frac{d^2 z^{i+1}}{dz^2} - \sum_{i=1}^{\infty} \frac{dz^i}{dz} = \frac{d^2[z^2/(1-z)]}{dz^2} - \frac{1}{(1-z)^2} = \frac{1+z}{(1-z)^3}$$

Using this identity with $q=1-z$, we have

$$E\{X^2\} = \sum_{i=1}^{\infty} i^2 q(1-q)^{i-1} = \frac{2-q}{q^2} = \frac{2-pq_r}{(pq_r)^2}$$

b) For an individual node, we have an M/G/1 queue with vacations. The vacations are deterministic with a duration of 1 slot, and the service time has the first and second moments found in part a). Thus, using Eq. (3.55) for the queueing delay and adding an extra service time to get the system delay,

$$T = \frac{(\lambda/m)E\{X^2\}}{2(1-\rho)} + \frac{1}{2} + \frac{1}{q} = \frac{\lambda(2-\rho)}{2q^2(1-\rho)m} + \frac{1}{2} + \frac{1}{q}$$

Since the arrival rate is λ/m and the service rate is q, we have $\rho = \lambda/(mq)$. Substituting this into the above expression for T and simplifying,

$$T = \frac{1}{q_r p(1-\rho)} + \frac{1-2\rho}{2(1-\rho)}$$

c) For $p=1$ and $q_r=1/m$, we have $\rho = \lambda$, so that

$$T = \frac{m}{1-\lambda} + \frac{1-2\lambda}{2(1-\lambda)}$$

In the limit of large m, this is twice the delay of TDM as given in Eq. (3.59).

4.9

a) Let v be the mean number of packets in the system. Given n packets in the system, with each packet independently transmitted in a slot with probability $v-1$, the probability of an idle slot, $P\{I|n\}$ is $(1-v-1)^n$. The joint probability of an idle slot and n packets in the system is then

$$P\{n,I\} = P\{n\}P\{I|n\} = \frac{\exp(-v)v^n}{n!}(1-v^{-1})^n$$

$$P\{I\} = \sum_{n=0}^{\infty} P\{n,I\} = \sum_{n=0}^{\infty} \frac{\exp(-v)\,(v-1)^n}{n!} = \frac{1}{e}$$

b) Using the results above, we can find $P\{n\,|\,I\}$

$$P\{n\,|\,I\} = \frac{P\{n,I\}}{P\{I\}} = \frac{\exp(-v+1)\,(v-1)^n}{n!}$$

Thus, this probability is Poisson with mean $v-1$.

c) We can find the joint probability of success and n in the system similarly

$$P\{n,S\} = P\{n\}P\{S\,|n\} = \frac{\exp(-v)\,v^n}{n!}\,n(1-v^{-1})^{n-1}v^{-1} = \frac{\exp(-v)\,(v-1)^{n-1}}{(n-1)!}$$

$$P\{S\} = \sum_{n=0}^{\infty} \frac{\exp(-v)\,(v-1)^{n-1}}{(n-1)!} = \frac{1}{e}$$

d) From this, the probability that there were n packets in the system given a success is

$$P\{n\,|S\} = \frac{P\{n,S\}}{P\{S\}} = \frac{\exp(-v+1)\,(v-1)^{n-1}}{(n-1)!}$$

Note that $n-1$ is the number of remaining packets in the system with the successful packet removed, and it is seen from above that this remaining number is Poisson with mean $v-1$.

4.10

a) All nodes are initially in mode 2, so when the first success occurs, the successful node moves to mode 1. While that node is in mode 1, it transmits in every slot, preventing any other node from entering mode 1. When that node eventually transmits all its packets and moves back to mode 2, we return to the initial situation of all nodes in mode 2. Thus at most one node at a time can be in mode 1.

b) The probability of successful transmission, p_1, is the probability that no other node is transmitting. Thus $p_1 = (1-q_r)^{m-1}$. The first and second moment of the time between successful transmissions is the same computation as in problem 4.8a. We have

$$\overline{X} = \frac{1}{p_1} \qquad\qquad \overline{X^2} = \frac{2-p_1}{p_1^2}$$

c) The probability of some successful dummy transmission in a given slot when all nodes are in mode 2 is $p_2 = mq_r(1-q_r)^{m-1}$. The first two moments of the time to such a success is the same problem as above, with p_2 in place of p_1. Thus

$$\overline{v} = \frac{1}{p_2} \qquad\qquad \overline{v^2} = \frac{2-p_2}{p_2^2}$$

d) The system is the same as the exhaustive multiuser system of subsection 3.5.2 except for the random choice of a new node to be serviced at the end of each reservation interval. Thus for the ith packet arrival to the system as a whole, the expected queueing delay before the given packet first attempts transmission is

$$E\{W_i\} = E\{R_i\} + E\{N_i\}\overline{X} + E\{Y_i\}$$

where R_i is the residual time to completion of the current packet service or reservation interval and Y_i is the duration of all the whole reservation intervals during which packet i must wait before its node enters mode 1. Since the order of serving packets is independent of their service time, $E\{N_i\} = \lambda E\{W\}$ in the limit as i approaches infinity. Also, since the length of each reservation interval is independent of the number of whole reservation intervals that the packet must wait, $E\{Y_i\}$ is the expected number of whole reservation intervals times the expected length of each. Thus

$$W = \frac{R + E\{S\}\overline{v}}{1-\rho}, \quad \rho = \lambda\overline{X}$$

e) As in Eq. (3.64),

$$R = \frac{\lambda\overline{X^2}}{2} + \frac{(1-\rho)\overline{v^2}}{2\overline{v}}$$

Finally, the number of whole reservation intervals that the packet must wait is zero with probability 1/m, one with probability (1-1/m)/m, and in general i with probability $(1-1/m)^i/m$. Thus $E\{S\} = m-1$. Substituting these results and those of parts b) and c) into the above expression for W, we get the desired expression.

4.11

a) Since all nodes receive feedback at the same time, and the first node involved in a collision waits one time unit for transmissions currently in progress to cease, all retransmissions must be successful. We assume here that if feedback for one collision arrives while previous retransmissions are taking place (this can happen if τ is large), then the new retransmissions follow the old. Under heavy loading, we note that many packets will typically arrive and become backlogged during the retransmissions for the previous period. These will all be transmitted (and thus establish a reservation order for retransmission) in the first time unit of the next reservation interval. Feedback for other collisions during the reservation interval will normally arrive before the retransmissions for these backlog collisions are completed. If τ is large, there will be occasional successful transmissions during the reservation period, but only a small fraction (about $e^{-2\lambda}$) of the transmissions during the reservation period are successful and only a small fraction of time is occupied by reservation periods. Thus it is reasonable to approximate all arrivals during one retransmission period and the following reservation period as being retransmitted in the following retransmission period. This corresponds to the partially gated single user system of subsection 3.5.2 with deterministic service X=1 and deterministic reservation period A=1+τ. From Eq. (3.73) with m=1, the queueing delay is then

$$W = \frac{\lambda}{2(1-\lambda)} + \frac{(1+\tau)(1+\lambda)}{2(1-\lambda)}$$

The system delay is $T = W+1$.

b) The above equation shows that W and T are finite for $\lambda < 1$

4.12

a) Let τ_i be the interval between the ith and $i+1^{th}$ initiation of a k packet transmission group; thus τ_i is exponentially distributed with rate G and $...\tau_{i-1}, \tau_i, ...$ are independent. The jth packet in the ith transmission group will be successful if $\tau_i \geq j$ and if $\tau_{i-1} \geq k-j+1$ (see the diagram below). Thus

$$P_{succ} = e^{-Gj} e^{-G(k-j+1)} = e^{-G(k+1)}$$

b) Since the group attempt rate is G, the packet attempt rate is Gk. A fraction $e^{-G(k+1)}$ of the packets are successful, so the throughput is $Gk\, e^{-G(k+1)}$. This is maximized by G = $1/(k+1)$, leading to a maximum throughput of $k/[e(k+1)]$. This can be made as close to $1/e$ as desired by increasing k.

4.13

a) The tree and the corresponding operations for each slot are shown below

Slot	Transmit Set	Waiting Sets	Feedback
1	S	-	e
2	L	R	0
3	R	-	e
4	RL	RR	e
5	RLL	RLR,RR	1
6	RLR	RR	1
7	RR	-	0

b) The second collision (i.e., that on slot 3) would have been avoided by the first improvement to the tree algorithm.

c) e,0,e,1,1; the final set, RR, would have been incorporated into the next collision resolution period in the second improvement.

4.14

Note that collisions correspond to non-leaf nodes of the tree and idles or successes correspond to leaves. In the process of building a binary tree from the root, we start with one leaf (the root). In each successive step, one leaf node is converted to a non-leaf node and two new leaves are added, yielding a net gain of one leaf and one non-leaf. Thus in a binary rooted tree, the number of leaves exceeds the number of non-leaves by one. This means that the total number of nodes (which is the number of slots in a CRP) is one plus twice the number of collisions. In Figure 4.9, there are four collisions and nine slots, as predicted.

For the alternate approach, note that the stack depth increases by one for each collision and decreases by one for each success or idle. Viewing the stack as starting with the original set (one element) on the stack and terminating with an empty stack, we see that the number of decreases exceeds the increases by one, leading to the same answer as above.

4.15

a) The probability of i packets joining the left subset, given k packets in the original set, is given by the binomial distribution

$$\frac{k! \, 2^{-k}}{i!(k-i)!}$$

b) Assuming $k \geq 2$, the CRP starts with an initial collision that takes one slot. Given that i packets go into the left subset, A_i is the expected number of additional slots required to transmit the left subset and A_{k-i} is the expected number on the right. Taking the expectation over the number i of packets in the left subset, we get the desired result,

$$A_k = 1 + \sum_{i=0}^{k} \frac{k! 2^{-k}}{i!(k-i)!} (A_i + A_{k-i})$$

c) Note that

$$\sum_{i=0}^{k} \frac{k! 2^{-k}}{i!(k-i)!} A_i = \sum_{i=0}^{k} \frac{k! 2^{-k}}{i!(k-i)!} A_{k-i}$$

Thus

$$A_k = 1 + 2\sum_{i=0}^{k} \frac{k! 2^{-k}}{i!(k-i)!} A_i = 1 + 2^{-k+1} A_k + 2\sum_{i=0}^{k-1} \frac{k! 2^{-k}}{i!(k-i)!} A_i$$

Taking the A_k term to the left side of the equation, we have

$$c_{ik} = \frac{k! 2^{-k+1}}{i!(k-i)!(1-2^{-k+1})} ; \quad i<k; \quad c_{kk} = \frac{1}{1-2^{-k+1}}$$

Evaluating this numerically, $A_2 = 5$ and $A_3 = 23/3$.

4.16

a) Given an original set of $k \geq 2$ packets and given that $i \geq 1$ packets join the left subset, the expected number of slots required is $1 + B_i + B_{k-i}$ (i.e., one slot for the original collision, B_i slots on the average for the left subset and B_{k-i} for the right. Given that $i=0$ packets join the left subset, however, the expected number of slots required is $1 + 1 + (B_k - 1)$ (i.e., one slot for the original collision, one for the left subset, and, since the first collision is avoided in the resolution of the right subset, $B_k - 1$ for that final resolution. Thus, since i is binomially distributed,

$$B_k = 1 + \sum_{i=1}^{k} \frac{k! 2^{-k}}{i!(k-i)!} (B_i + B_{k-i}) + 2^{-k} B_k$$

$$= 1 + \sum_{i=1}^{k-1} \frac{k! 2^{-k}}{i!(k-i)!} (B_i + B_{k-i}) + 2^{-k+1} B_k + 2^{-k} B_0$$

b) Noting the symmetry between i and $k-i$ above, noting that $B_0 = 1$, and taking the B_k terms to the left,

$$B_k(1-2^{-k+1}) = 1 + 2^{-k} + \sum_{i=1}^{k-1} \frac{k! 2^{-k+1}}{i!(k-i)!} B_i$$

$$C'_{kk} = \frac{1+2^{-k}}{1-2^{-k+1}} \qquad C'_{ik} = \frac{k! 2^{-k+1}}{i!(k-i)!(1-2^{-k+1})} \quad ; \, i<k$$

4.17

a) The joint event $X_L = 0$ and $X_L + X_R \geq 2$ is equivalent to $X_L = 0$ and $X_R \geq 2$, so

$$P\{X_L=0 \mid X_L+X_R \geq 2\} = \frac{P\{X_L=0\}P\{X_R \geq 2\}}{P\{X_L+X_R \geq 2\}} = \frac{e^{-G}[1-(1+G)e^{-G}]}{1-(1+2G)e^{-2G}}$$

This uses the fact that X_L and X_R are independent and $X=X_L+X_R$ is Poisson with mean $2G$. The other equalities use these same facts.

b) $\quad P\{X_L=1 \mid X_L+X_R \geq 2\} = \dfrac{P\{X_L=1\}P\{X_R \geq 1\}}{P\{X_L+X_R \geq 2\}} = \dfrac{Ge^{-G}(1-e^{-G})}{1-(1+2G)e^{-2G}}$

c) $\quad P\{X_L \geq 2 \mid X_L+X_R \geq 2\} = \dfrac{P\{X_L \geq 2\}P\{X_R \geq 0\}}{P\{X_L+X_R \geq 2\}} = \dfrac{1-(1+G)e^{-G}}{1-(1+2G)e^{-2G}}$

d) $P\{X_R=1 \mid X_L=1, X_L+X_R\geq2\} = \dfrac{P\{X_R=1\}P\{X_L=1\}}{P\{X_L=1\}P\{X_R\geq1\}} = \dfrac{Ge^{-G}}{1-e^{-G}}$

Note that this is just $P\{X_R=1 \mid X_R\geq1\}$.

e) $P\{X_R=i \mid X_L=0, X_L+X_R\geq2\} = \dfrac{P\{X_R=i\}P\{X_L=0\}}{P\{X_L=0\}P\{X_R\geq2\}} = \dfrac{G^i e^{-G}}{i! \,[1-(1+G)e^{-G}]}$

Note that this is $P\{X_R=i \mid X_R\geq2\}$.

f) $P\{X_R=i \mid X_L\geq2, X_L+X_R\geq2\} = \dfrac{P\{X_R=i\}P\{X_L\geq2\}}{P\{X_L\geq2\}} = \dfrac{G^i e^{-G}}{i!}$

Note that this is $P\{X_R=i\}$.

4.18

a) and b)

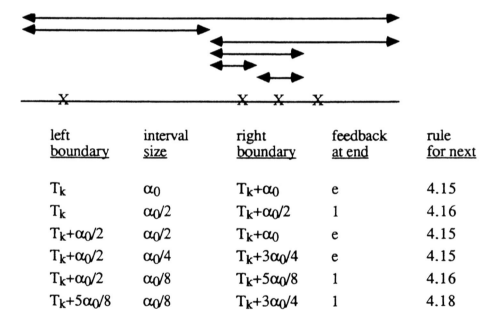

left boundary	interval size	right boundary	feedback at end	rule for next
T_k	α_0	$T_k+\alpha_0$	e	4.15
T_k	$\alpha_0/2$	$T_k+\alpha_0/2$	1	4.16
$T_k+\alpha_0/2$	$\alpha_0/2$	$T_k+\alpha_0$	e	4.15
$T_k+\alpha_0/2$	$\alpha_0/4$	$T_k+3\alpha_0/4$	e	4.15
$T_k+\alpha_0/2$	$\alpha_0/8$	$T_k+5\alpha_0/8$	1	4.16
$T_k+5\alpha_0/8$	$\alpha_0/8$	$T_k+3\alpha_0/4$	1	4.18

c) The diagram below shows the path through the Markov chain for the given sequence of events:

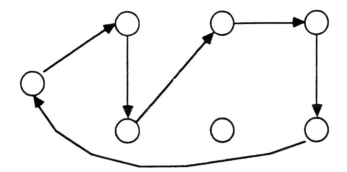

4.19

a) Consider first the expected number of successes on all but the final slot of a CRP and then the expected number on the final slot. Each non-final success occurs on a left interval, and, in terms of the Markov chain of Figure 4.13, corresponds to a transition from a left interval (top row of states) to a right interval (bottom row of states). Thus, for any given CRP, the number of non-final successes is the number of transitions from left to right states. Since the right states ($i \geq 1$) are entered only by these transitions, the number of non-final successes is the number of visits to right states (other than the state (R,0). Thus the expected number of non-final successes is the expected number of visits to right states, $i \geq 1$. Finally note that, except when the CRP consists only of a single idle slot (which occurs with probability $\exp(-G_0)$), the final slot of a CRP is a success. Thus

$$\bar{n} = 1 - \exp(-G_0) + \sum_{i=1}^{\infty} p(R,i)$$

b) Whenever a collision occurs in a left interval, the corresponding right interval is returned to the waiting interval. The number of packets successfully transmitted in a CRP is the number in the original allocation interval less the number returned by the mechanism above. Thus the expected number transmitted is the expected number in the original interval less the expected number returned; this is true despite statistical dependencies between the original number and the returned number. Given that an interval of size x is returned, the number of packets in the returned interval is Poisson with mean λx, independent of the past history of the CRP. Thus, given that a fraction f of the interval is returned (via one or more intervals), the expected number of returns is $\lambda \alpha_0 f$. Averaging over f (which is dependent on the number in the original interval), the expected number of returns is $\lambda \alpha_0 E\{f\}$. Thus

$$\bar{n} = \lambda \alpha_0 [1 - E\{f\}]$$

4.20

Let n_k (or n, suppressing the subscript for slot time) be the backlog at slot k and assume n is Poisson with known mean v. Each of the n packets is independently transmitted in slot k with probability $q_r(v)$, so the probability that the kth slot is idle, given n, is $P\{I|n\} = [1-q_r(v)]^n$. Thus the joint probability of n backlogged packets and an idle slot is

$$P\{n,I\} = P\{n\}P\{I \mid n\} = \frac{\exp(-v)v^n}{n!}[1-q_r(v)]^n$$

$$P\{I\} = \sum_{n=0}^{\infty} P\{n,I\} = \sum_{n=0}^{\infty} \frac{\exp(-v)[v-vq_r(v)]^n}{n!} = \exp[-vq_r(v)]$$

$$P\{n \mid I\} = \frac{P\{n,I\}}{P\{I\}} = \frac{\exp[-v+vq_r(v)]\,[v-vq_r(v)]^n}{n!}$$

Thus, this probability is Poisson with mean $v-vq_r(v)$. Next consider a success

$$P\{n,S\} = P\{n\}P\{S \mid n\} = \frac{\exp(-v)\,v^n}{n!}\,n[1-q_r(v)]^{n-1}q_r(v)$$

$$= \frac{\exp(-v)\,[v-vq_r(v)]^{n-1}vq_r(v)}{(n-1)!}$$

$$P\{S\} = \sum_{n=1}^{\infty} P\{n,S\} = vq_r(v)\exp(-v)\sum_{n=1}^{\infty}\frac{[v-vq_r(v)]^{n-1}}{(n-1)!} = vq_r(v)\exp[-vq_r(v)]$$

$$P\{n \mid S\} = \frac{\exp[-v+vq_r(v)]\,[v-vq_r(v)]^{n-1}}{(n-1)!}$$

This says that the aposteriori distribution of n-1, given S, is Poisson with mean $v-vq_r(v)$.

4.21

a) Since X_1 and X_2 are non-negative random variables, $\max(X_1, X_2) \le X_1+X_2$ for all sample values. Taking expectations,

$$\overline{Y} \le 2\overline{X} = 2$$

Suppose X takes values β with probability $1-\varepsilon$ and $k\beta$ with probability ε. Since

$$\overline{X} = \beta(1-\varepsilon) + k\beta\varepsilon = 1, \quad \text{we have} \quad \varepsilon = \frac{1-\beta}{\beta(k-1)}$$

Y takes on the value β with probability $(1-\varepsilon)^2$ and the value $k\beta$ with probability $2\varepsilon-\varepsilon^2$, so

$$\overline{Y} = \beta[1+(k-1)(2\varepsilon-\varepsilon^2)] = \beta + (1-\beta)(2-\varepsilon)$$

As k gets large, ε gets small and the final ε in the above expression is negligible. Thus, for small β, $E\{Y\} \approx 2$.

b) With a collision between two packets, the time until both transmissions are finished is the maximum of the two transmission times; the expected value of this is at most 2 from a), and the following idle slot adds a final β (A more refined analysis, using β as the minimum packet length, would show that $E\{Y\} \le 2-\beta$, so the final β could be omitted).

c) The time between state transitions is β with probability $e^{-g(n)}$, $(1+\beta)$ with probability $g(n)e^{-g(n)}$, and at most $(2+\beta)$ with probability $[g^2(n)/2]e^{-g(n)}$ (ignoring collisions of more than two packets). Thus the expected time between transitions is at most

$$\beta e^{-g(n)} + (1+\beta)g(n)e^{-g(n)} + (1+\beta/2)g^2(n)e^{-g(n)}$$

d) The success probability in state n is $g(n)e^{-g(n)}$, so the expected number of departures per unit time is the ratio of this to expected time between transitions (this can be justified rigorously by renewal theory). Thus the expected number of departures per unit time is at least

$$\frac{g(n)e^{-g(n)}}{\beta e^{-g(n)} + (1+\beta)g(n)e^{-g(n)} +(1+\beta/2)g^2(n)e^{-g(n)}} = \frac{g(n)}{\beta+(1+\beta)g(n)+(1+\beta/2)g^2(n)}$$

e) Taking the derivative of this with respect to g(n), we find a maximum where $g^2(n) = \beta/(1+\beta/2)$. Thus for small β, g(n) is approximately the square root of β. Substituting this back into the expression in d), the maximum throughput (i.e., departures per unit time), is approximately $1-2\sqrt{\beta}$.

4.22

a) Let ν be the mean of the number n of backlogged packets. Then the unconditional probability density of the time to the first packet transmission attempt is

$$p(\tau) = \sum_{n=0}^{\infty} p(\tau|n)P\{n\} = \sum_{n=0}^{\infty}(\lambda+xn)\exp[-(\lambda+xn)\tau]\frac{e^{-\nu}\nu^n}{n!}$$

$$= \sum_{n=0}^{\infty}(\lambda+xn)\exp(-\lambda\tau-\nu)\frac{(\nu e^{-x\tau})^n}{n!}$$

Splitting this into two terms, the first multiplied by λ and the second by xn, we get

$$p(\tau) = (\lambda + x\nu e^{-\tau x})\exp[-\lambda\tau-\nu+\nu e^{-x\tau}]$$

b) The joint probability of a backlog n, a backlogged packet starting first (denoted by b), and a starting time τ (as a density) is given by

$$P\{n,b,\tau\} = \frac{xne^{-(\lambda+xn)\tau}e^{-\nu}\nu^n}{n!} = \frac{xe^{-\lambda\tau-\nu}(\nu e^{-x\tau})^n}{(n-1)}$$

Using the result in a),

$$P\{n,b \mid \tau\} = \frac{xv'}{\lambda + v'} \; \frac{v'^{n-1}\exp(-v')}{(n-1)!}$$

where $v' = ve^{-\iota x}$.

c) The joint probability of backlog n, a new arrival starting first (denoted by a), and starting time τ (as a density) is given by

$$P\{n,a,\tau\} = \frac{\lambda e^{-(\lambda+nx)\tau} e^{-v} v^n}{n!} = \frac{\lambda e^{-\lambda\tau-v}(e^{-x\tau}v)^n}{n!}$$

$$P\{n,a \mid \tau\} = \frac{\lambda}{\lambda + xv'} \; \frac{v'^n\exp(-v')}{n!}; \quad v' = ve^{-\tau x}$$

d) Let n' be n-1 if a backlogged packet starts and n' be n if a new arrival starts. Adding the result in b) to that in c), we have

$$P\{n' \mid \tau\} = \frac{v'^{n'}\exp(-v')}{n'!}$$

That is, n' is Poisson with mean $v' = ve^{-\iota x}$.

4.23

In both systems, the maximum throughput depends on what happens with large backlogs. For slotted Aloha, the expected number of transmissions in state n (for n large) is g(n), which is optimally chosen as $\sqrt{(2\beta)}$. For large backlogs, the state can be estimated relatively accurately, so that the probability of a successful slot following any given idle slot is approximately $\sqrt{(2\beta)}$. For the FCFS algorithm, the allocation interval at the beginning of a CRP is chosen to make $\sqrt{(2\beta)}$ the probability of an initial successful slot. Thus, the two systems perform in essentially the same way except when a collision is being resolved in the FCFS algorithm. On the first slot after a collision, the FCFS algorithm sends a fraction $\sqrt{\beta}$ of the colliding interval, which yields a success with probability approximately $2\sqrt{\beta}$. This is an improvement over slotted Aloha, and the improvement is still greater on the right interval of the CRP. Thus the number of idle slots required to transmit the next two packets after a collision for FCFS is smaller than for slotted Aloha. However, for small β, collisions occur in slotted Aloha on a fraction of packets roughly equal to g, which is $\sqrt{(2\beta)}$; the additional idle time required for each of these is proportional to $\sqrt{\beta}$. This means that the idle time per packet to resolve collisions in slotted Aloha is proportional to β, which is negligible to order $\sqrt{\beta}$.

4.24

a) Let E{t} be the expected time between initiations of successful packet transmissions, assuming a backlogged system with the number of transmissions after each idle slot having a Poisson distribution with mean g. Using the same argument as in Eq. (4.43), but recognizing that the time occupied by a collision is now 2β, including the idle slot after the collision, we have

$$E\{t\} = [\beta+E\{t\}]e^{-g} + [1+\beta]ge^{-g} + [2\beta+E\{t\}][1-(1+g)e^{-g}]$$

$$E\{t\} = \frac{\beta e^{-g} + (1+\beta)ge^{-g} + 2\beta[1-(1+g)e^{-g}]}{ge^{-g}} = 1 + \frac{\beta(2e^{g}-1-g)}{g}$$

Minimizing numerically gives $E\{t\} = 1 + 3.31\beta$ at $g = 0.77$.

b) Using Little's relation on the time average of Eq. (4.42),

$$W = \frac{\overline{R} + \overline{y}}{1-\lambda E\{t\}} = \frac{\overline{R} + \overline{y}}{1-\lambda(1+3.31\beta)}$$

c) For small β, the contribution of the idle and collision intervals to the residual time R can be ignored since they are proportional to β^2. Thus,

$$\overline{R} \approx \frac{\lambda E\{(X+\beta)^2\}}{2} \approx \frac{\lambda\overline{X^2} + 2\lambda\beta}{2}$$

As in CSMA,

$$\overline{y} = E\{t\} - (1+\beta) = 2.31\beta$$

Substituting these results into the result in part b),

$$W \approx \frac{\lambda\overline{X^2} + \beta(4.62+2\lambda)}{2[1-\lambda(1+3.31\beta)]}$$

d) Clearly the Poisson approximation is very poor for a backlog of one, since collisions cannot occur. On the other hand, each interval t_i involves at least a backlog of two, so the effect of backlogs of one is seen only in the expected value of y, which is almost negligible.

4.25

We want to find the maximum time from when a given node starts to transmit in a collision until that node both stops transmitting and hears the channel become idle. Suppose a given node j starts to transmit at time t. By time $t+\beta$ all other nodes must have ceased transmission. Thus, by time $t+2\beta$, node j ceases to hear these other transmissions. On the other hand, since by assumption a collision occurred, at least one other node started to transmit before $t+\beta$, so that node j must have ceased transmission also by $t+2\beta$. Note, however, that the definition of a collision is somewhat fuzzy. For example two nodes at one end of a bus could start transmitting almost simultaneously and then stop very quickly. A node at the other end of the bus could start transmitting almost b time units later and then stop almost immediately because of the detected collision. A node at the first end of the bus, having heard the collision from the first two nodes cease, could start transmitting just before hearing the transmission from the second end of the bus, and another node at the second end could start transmitting after another β time units. Thus even though each node hears the channel become idle at most 2β time units after being involved in a collision, later collisions could be regarded as part of the same larger collision event.

4.26

a) The first transmission after a given idle detection will be successful if no other transmission starts within the next β time units. Since the process of initiations is Poisson with rate G, the probability of this is

$$P_{succ} = e^{-\beta G}$$

b) The mean time until the first initiation after an idle detection is 1/G (note that all nodes detect the channel as being idle at the same time). If this first initiation is successful, $1+\beta$ time units are required until the next idle detection; if the initiation is unsuccessful, 2β time units are required. Thus

$$E\{\text{time between idle detects}\} = G^{-1} + (1+\beta)e^{-\beta G} + 2\beta(1-e^{-\beta G})$$

c) The throughput T is the ratio of P_{succ} to the expected time between idle detects,

$$T = \frac{e^{-\beta G}}{G^{-1}+(1+\beta)e^{-\beta G}+2\beta(1-e^{-\beta G})} = \frac{1}{(G^{-1}+2\beta)e^{\beta G}+(1-\beta)}$$

d) We can maximize this by minimizing 1/T. Taking the derivative of 1/T with respect to G and setting it equal to 0, we find that the minimum of 1/T occurs at $\beta G = 1/2$. Substituting this into the expression for T, we get

$$T = \frac{1}{1+\beta(4\sqrt{e}-1)} = \frac{1}{1+5.595\beta}$$

4.27

Each packet transmission is effectively extended by a round trip delay, mv. That is, if X is the time for a node to transmit a given packet plus token, then X is extended to X+mv if the token is not sent until the packet has returned to the sending node. The effective utilization factor then becomes $\rho = \lambda(E\{X\}+mv) = \lambda(1+mv)$. Using Eq. (3.76) with these modified values for ρ and X, we have

$$W = \frac{\overline{\lambda(X+mv)^2} + [m+\lambda(1+mv)]v}{2[1-\lambda(1+mv+v)]}$$

Note that if the round trip delay is large relative to the packet transmission time, this causes a major increase in delay and a major decrease in maximum throughput.

4.28

Suppose a given node has a full transit buffer, and suppose the previous node on the ring has a never empty input buffer. Then that previous node will send a constant stream of packets (either from its transit buffer or input buffer) to the given node. If none of these packets are addressed to the given node, the hapless node must continue to transmit from its transit buffer, which remains full due to the constant input. In essence, in a fully loaded register insertion ring, the nodes that receive the most traffic are the ones permitted to transmit the most traffic. This problem could, of course, be overcome by a more complex protocol that prevents nodes from monopolizing the ring.

4.29

Given the placement of the first node at a given distance X_1 from the left end of the bus, the other node will be to the left of the first node with probability X_1 and to the right with probability $1-X_1$. Given that it is to the left, its expected distance from X_1 is $X_1/2$, and given that it is to the right, its expected distance is $(1-X_1)/2$. Thus the expected distance between X_1 and X_2, given X_1, is

$$E\{|X_2-X_1| \mid X_1\} = \frac{(X_1)^2}{2} + \frac{(1-X_1)^2}{2}$$

Averaging over X_1, we then have

$$E\{|X_2-X_1|\} = \int_0^1 \frac{(X_1)^2}{2} + \frac{(1-X_1)^2}{2} \, dX_1 = \frac{1}{3}$$

4.30

a) Node i is the lowest numbered node with a packet to send if nodes 0, 1, ..., i-1 have no packets (which occurs with probability $(1-q)^i$) and node i has a packet. Thus

$$P\{i\} = q(1-q)^i ; \quad i \geq 0.$$

b) $k \geq 0$ is the number of successive sets of 2^j nodes that contain no packets. Thus $k+1$ sets of 2^j nodes each must be tested to find the first set with a packet, and j additional tests are necessary to find i within the final set of 2^j. Thus the required number of reservation slots is $k+1+j$.

c) For a given value of j, the expected number of reservation slots is $E\{k\}+1+j$. By the suggested approximation $k = i2^{-j}$, we have $E\{k\} = 2^{-j}E\{i\}$. Thus

$$E\{k\} = 2^{-j} \sum_{i=1}^{\infty} iq(1-q)^i = 2^{-j}q(1-q) \sum_{i=1}^{\infty} i(1-q)^{i-1} = 2^{-j}\frac{1-q}{q}$$

$$E\{\text{reservation slots}\} = 2^{-j}\frac{1-q}{q} + 1 + j$$

It is not much more difficult to find the exact value of $E\{k\}$. We note that k is the integer part of $i2^{-j}$, and thus $P\{k \geq n\} = P\{i \geq n2^j\}$. We then have

$$E\{k\} = \sum_{k=1}^{\infty} kP\{k\} = \sum_{n=1}^{\infty} P\{k \geq n\} = \sum_{n=1}^{\infty} P\{i \geq n2^j\}$$

$$= \sum_{n=1}^{\infty} \exp[n2^j \ln(1-q)] = \frac{\exp[n2^j \ln(1-q)]}{1 - \exp[n2^j \ln(1-q)]}$$

The exact value of $E\{k\}$ is less than the approximate value by a quantity somewhat less than 1/2.

d) Using the approximation for $E\{k\}$ again, we want to choose the integer $j \geq 0$ that minimizes $E\{\text{reservation slots}\}$. Observe that the expression for $E\{\text{reservation slots}\}$ above (temporarily regarding j as a real number) has a positive second derivative with respect to j. Thus the expression is minimized over integer $j \geq 0$ by choosing the smallest integer j for which the expression increases in going from j to $j+1$, i.e, for which

$$2^{-j}\frac{1-q}{q} + 1 + j < 2^{-j-1}\frac{1-q}{q} + 2 + j$$

This means that the minimum occurs at the smallest value of j for which $2^{j+1} > (1-q)/q$. Thus the minimizing j is the integer part of $\log_2[(1-q)/q]$.

We can find the minimizing j for $E\{\text{reservation slots}\}$ using the exact expression for $E\{k\}$ in the same way. Let $f(j) = \exp[2^j \ln(1-q)]$ and note that $f(j+1) = f^2(j)$. Thus we want to find the smallest value of j for which

$$\frac{f(j)}{1-f(j)} < \frac{f^2(j)}{1-f^2(j)} + 1$$

This inequality is equivalent to $f(j) < 1 - f^2(j)$. The two sides of this inequality are equal for $f(j) = (\sqrt{5} - 1)/2$, so the minimizing j is the smallest integer j for which $f(j) < (\sqrt{5} - 1)/2$. Thus j is the smallest integer for which $2^j \ln(1-q) < \ln[(\sqrt{5} - 1)/2]$.

4.31

a) A simultaneous transmission on links 1 and 3 causes a collision for the transmission on link 1; similarly, a collision on link 2 occurs if 2 and 3 are used simultaneously. Finally, simultaneous transmissions on links 1 and 2 cause a collision for both transmissions. Thus at most one link can be used successfully at a time and $f_1+f_2+f_3 \leq 1$. To view this in terms of Eq. (4.75), we let x_1, x_2, and x_3 be the collision free vectors (100), (010), and (001) respectively, and we let x_4 be the trivial CFV (000). Then, for $1 \leq i \leq 3$, f_i corresponds to a_i in Eq. (4.75) and the constraints $a_i \geq 0$ and $a_1+a_2+a_3+a_4=1$ is equivalent to $f_1+f_2+f_3 \leq 1$.

b) From Eq. (4.77), we have

$$p_1 = (1-q_3)(1-q_2)$$

$$p_2 = (1-q_3)(1-q_1)$$

$$p_3 = 1$$

Eq. (4.78) then gives us the fractional utilizations

$$f = f_1 = q_1(1-q_3)(1-q_2) \qquad \text{(i)}$$

$$f = f_2 = q_2(1-q_3)(1-q_1) \qquad \text{(ii)}$$

$$2f = f_3 = q_3 \qquad \text{(iii)}$$

Taking the ratio of (ii) and (i),

$$1 = \frac{q_2(1-q_1)}{q_1(1-q_2)} \; ; \qquad \text{thus } q_1 = q_2$$

c) Using $q_1 = q_2$ and $q_3 = 2f$ in (i) above, we have $f = q_1(1-2f)(1-q_1)$. Thus

$$\frac{f}{1-2f} = q_1(1-q_1) \le \frac{1}{4}$$

The inequality above follows by taking the maximum of $q_1(1-q_1)$ over q_1 between 0 and 1. It follows from this that $f \le 1/6$.

4.32

Let q_i be the attempt rate on link i and p_i be the probability of successful transmission on link i. A transmission on link 1 will be successful if no transmission is simultaneously taking place on link 3 (since link 5 is never used). Thus, assuming independent attempts, $p_1 = 1-q_3$. Similarly, a transmission on link 2 is successful if link 4 is not simultaneously carrying transmitting, so $p_2 = 1-q_4$. Transmissions on links 3 and 4 are always successful, so $p_3 = 1$ and $p_4 = 1$. Finally, a transmission on link 7 is successful if neither links 3 nor 4 are carrying transmissions simultaneously, so $p_3 = (1-q_3)(1-q_4)$. Eq. (4.78) states that the throughput on each link, f_i, is equal to $p_i q_i$. Combining these equations with the values for p_i found above and with the given throughputs, we have the equations

$$1/3 = f_1 = q_1(1-q_3)$$

$$1/3 = f_2 = q_2(1-q_4)$$

$$1/3 = f_3 = q_3$$

$$1/3 = f_4 = q_4$$

$$4/9 = f_7 = q_7(1-q_3)(1-q_4)$$

These throughputs will be feasible (under the assumptions given) if we can find values between 0 and 1 for the attempt rates q_i that satisfy these equations and if the node transmission rates are also between 0 and 1. The third and fourth equations show that $q_3 =$

$q_4 = 1/3$. Using these values in the first two equations, we find that $q_1 = q_2 = 1/2$. This indicates that the attempt rate from the left most node is 1, which is permissible. Finally, using $q_3 = q_4 = 1/3$ in the final equation gives us $q_7 = 1$. Thus we see that the given throughputs are feasible. The success probabilities are then easily found to be $p_1 = p_2 = 2/3$, $p_3 = p_4 = 1$, and $p_7 = 4/9$.

b) Since links 1 and 2 can not be used simultaneously, and links 3 and 4 always transmit on the slot following a successful transmission from 1 or 2 respectively, links 3 and 4 cannot be used simultaneously. Thus 2/3 of the slots are used to carry packets on either links 3 or 4. Thus at most 1/3 of the slots can carry packets successfully on link 7. What has happened here is that the assumption that nodes transmit independently of each other has been violated by the fact that links 3 and 4 are both forwarding traffic from the same node.

c) Since links 1 and 2 carry packets alternately, two successive attempts are never made on link 1, and thus (since link 3 always transmits only on the slot after receiving a packet on link 1) no packet on link 1 is ever subject to a collision. The same result holds for link 2, and thus $f_1 = f_2 = f_3 = f_4 = 1/2$. In this case, links 3 and 4 transmit on alternate slots, and all packets on link 7 suffer collisions.

4.33

The token arrival times, starting at t_1, are 4, 5, 6, 8, 9, 10, 12, 13, 14,.... . This can be expressed analytically as $t_i = 3+i +\lfloor(i-1)/3\rfloor$ for $i \geq 1$. The result as given in the bound is $t_i = i+2+\lfloor i/3\rfloor$ for $i \geq 1$. The corresponding token times, starting at t_1, are 4, 5, 7, 8, 9, 11, 12, 13, ... The difference results from the bound taking t_0 as τ rather than as 0.

4.34

From Eq. (4.82), we see that the asymptotic round trip token time is $\tau m/(m+1) + T/(m+1)$. Node i receives α_i of that time for high priority traffic and $(\tau-T)/(m+1)$ for low priority traffic. Thus the fraction of traffic received by node i is

$$\frac{\alpha_i(m+1)}{\tau m+T} \text{ high priority; } \quad \frac{(\tau-T)m}{\tau m+T} \text{ low priority}$$

Fortunately this adds up to 1.

b) Since each node i requires only a fraction α_i/τ of the ring capacity for its high priority traffic, a fraction $(\tau-T)/\tau$ is left over for low priority. Since this is shared equally by each node, each node receives $(\tau-T)/(m\tau)$ for low priority traffic.

4.35

First assume A=1 and C1>0 where C1 is the value in counter 1.

> On the arrival of an idle slot in the downstream direction, decrement C1.
> On the arrival of a request bit in the upstream direction, increment C2 (the value of counter 2).

Next assume A=1 and C1=0.

On the arrival of an idle slot in the downstream direction,
   1) Place the frame in the idle slot, setting the busy bit;
   2) If there is a waiting frame in the supplementary queue, put it in the virtual queue, place C2 in counter 1 and set C2 to 0;
   3) If there is no waiting frame, set A=0.
On the arrival of a request bit in the upstream direction, increment C2.

Next assume A=0.

On the arrival of an idle slot in the downstream direction, decrement C2.
On the arrival of a request bit in the upstream direction, increment C2.
On the arrival of a frame to be transmitted, put it in the virtual queue, place C2 in counter 1 and set C2 to 0.

Chapter 5 Solutions

5.1

The Prim-Dijkstra Algorithm   Arbitrarily select node e as the initial fragment. Arcs are added in the following order: (d, e), (b, d), (b, c) {tie with (a, b) is broken arbitrarily}, (a, b), (a, f).

Kruskal's Algorithm   Start with each node as a fragment. Arcs are added in the following order: (a,f), (b,d), (a,b) {tie with (b,c) is broken arbitrarily}, (b,c), (d,e).
The weight of the MST in both cases is 15.

5.2

The Bellman-Ford Algorithm   By convention, $D_1^{(h)} = 0$, for all h. Initially $D_1^{(1)} = d_{1i}$, for all $i \neq 1$. For each successive $h \geq 1$ we compute $D_i^{(h+1)} = \min_j [D_j^{(h)} + d_{ji}]$, for all $i \neq 1$. The results are summarized in the following table.

i	D_i^1	D_i^2	D_i^3	D_i^4	D_i^5	Shortest path arcs†
1	0	0	0	0	0	
2	4	4	4	4	4	$(1, 2)$
3	5	5	5	5	5	$(1, 3)$
4	∞	7	7	7	7	$(2, 4)$
5	∞	14	13	12	12	$(6, 5)$
6	∞	14	10	10	10	$(4, 6)$
7	∞	∞	16	12	12	$(6, 7)$

†The arcs on the shortest path tree are computed *after* running the Bellman-Ford algorithm. For each $i \neq 1$ we include in the shortest path tree one arc (j,i) that minimizes Bellman's equation.

Dijkstra's Algorithm   Refer to the algorithm description in the text. Initially: $D_1 = 0$; $D_i = d_{1i}$ for $i \neq 1$; $P = \{1\}$. The state after each iteration is shown in the table below. P is not shown but can be inferred from i. Only the D_j's which are updated at each step are shown.

Iteration	i	D_1	D_2	D_3	D_4	D_5	D_6	D_7	Arc added
initial		0	4	5	∞	∞	∞	∞	
1	2			5	7	14	∞	∞	$(1,2)$
2	3				7	14	14	∞	$(1,3)$
3	4					13	10	∞	$(2,4)$
4	6					12		12	$(4,6)$
5	5							12	$(6,5)$
6	7								$(6,7)$

5.3

Let p_{ij} be the probability that link (i,j) fails during the lifetime of a virtual circuit. Let P_k be the probability that a path $k = (A, i, \ldots, j, B)$ remains intact. Since links fail independently we have:

$$P_k = (1 - p_{Ai}) \cdots (1 - p_{jB})$$

We want to find the path k for which P_k is maximized. Equivalently, we can find the path k for which $-\ln P_k$ is minimized.

$$-\ln P_k = -\ln(1 - p_{Ai}) - \cdots - \ln(1 - p_{jB})$$

Since the arc weights p_{ij} are small, $1 - p_{ij}$ is close to 1 and we may use the approximation $\ln z \approx z - 1$. This gives:

$$-\ln P_k \approx p_{Ai} + \cdots + p_{jB}$$

Therefore, the most reliable path from A to B is the shortest path using the weights given in the figure. Applying Dijkstra's algorithm gives the shortest path tree. We proceed as in problem 5.2.

Iteration	i	D_A	D_B	D_C	D_D	D_E	D_F	D_G	Arc added
initial		0	∞	0.01	∞	0.03	∞	∞	
1	C		∞		0.06	0.02	∞	∞	(A,C)
2	E		∞		0.04		0.06	∞	(C,E)
3	D		0.1				0.05	0.06	(E,D)
4	F		0.1					0.06	(D,F)
5	G		0.09						(D,G)
6	B								(G,B)

The most reliable path from A to B is (A, C, E, D, G, B). The probability that this path remains intact is

$$P_{ACEDGB} = (0.99)(0.99)(0.98)(0.98)(0.97) = 0.913$$

5.4

Let the weights for arcs AB, BC, and CA be 1, 2, and 2, respectively. Then an MST is $\{AB, BC\}$ whereas the shortest path tree rooted at C is $\{CA, CB\}$.

5.5

a) We consider the following network with an initial routing similar to example 1 in 5.2.5. A routing can be completely specified by indicating the link at which

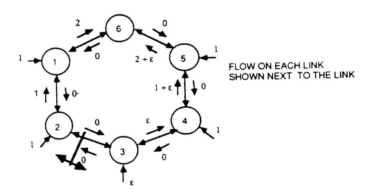

FLOW ON EACH LINK
SHOWN NEXT TO THE LINK

the traffic changes from clockwise to counterclockwise. This link always carries zero traffic in both directions. For example, the routing in the above diagram would be called (2,3). With this as the initial routing, the subsequent routings would be: (4,5), (1,6), (5,6), (1,6)....

b) We proceed as in **a)** but add 1 to each length.

With an initial routing of (2,3), subsequent routings are: (3,4), (2,3).... Notice that the oscillations have been damped as compared to part **a)**, and a reasonable routing is always maintained.

With an initial routing of (1,2), subsequent routings are: (4,5), (1,2).... There are still undesirable oscillations, but the situation is not quite as bad as in **a)**.

With an initial routing of (1,6), subsequent routings are: (5,6), (1,6).... For this initial condition, the constant bias factor has had no effect on the oscillatory behavior.

By symmetry, the remaining three cases are equivalent to the above.

c) Notice that regardless of the choice of α, node 3 reverses its routing at each iteration. Therefore, the best that can be hoped for is oscillation between the two reasonable routings (2,3) and (3,4). In order to reduce oscillations with a routing of (1,6), node 5 must continue to route counterclockwise. This requires that:

$$5\alpha > \alpha + 4 + \epsilon \quad \Rightarrow \quad \alpha > 1 + \epsilon/4$$

In order to reduce oscillations with a routing of (1,2), node 4 must continue to route counterclockwise. This requires that:

$$4\alpha + 1 > 2\alpha + 5 + 2\epsilon \quad \Rightarrow \quad \alpha > 2 + \epsilon$$

By symmetry, the remaining routings result is the same conditions. Therefore, for values of $\alpha > 2 + \epsilon$ the routing of all nodes except node 3 eventually remains constant.

d) For this particular example, the averaging changes the link lengths, but has no effect on the routing decisions. The resulting routings are the same as in part **a)**.

5.6

(a) Let D_i be the shortest distance from node i to node 1 corresponding to lengths d_{ij}. We claim that

$$D_i \le D_i^0, \qquad \forall\, i.$$

Given the definition of D_i^0, it will suffice to show that

$$D_i \le \tilde{D}_i, \qquad \forall\, i \notin \cup_k N_k \cup \{1\}.$$

Indeed consider any node $i \notin \cup_k N_k \cup \{1\}$, and let $\tilde{P}_i$ be a shortest path from i to 1 corresponding to lengths $\tilde{d}_{ij}$. We have $\tilde{D}_m = \tilde{d}_{mn} + \tilde{D}_n$ for all arcs (m,n) of $\tilde{P}_i$, so by the definition of the sets N_k, we must have $d_{mn} \le \tilde{d}_{mn}$ for all arcs (m,n) of $\tilde{P}_i$. Therefore, the length of P_i with respect to arc lengths d_{ij} is no more than its length with respect to arc lengths $\tilde{d}_{ij}$, implying that $D_i \le \tilde{D}_i$. Thus we have $D_i \le \tilde{D}_i$ for all $i \notin \cup_k N_k \cup \{1\}$ and $D_i \le D_i^0$ for all i.

Now consider the Bellman-Ford method corresponding to arc lengths d_{ij} and starting from two different initial conditions. The first set of initial conditions is the standard $\hat{D}_i^0 = \infty$ for $i \ne 1$ and $\hat{D}_1^0 = 0$, and the corresponding iterates are denoted $\hat{D}_i^h$. The second set of initial conditions is D_i^0 as given in the problem statement and the corresponding iterates are denoted D_i^h. Since

$$D_i \le D_i^0 \le \hat{D}_i^0, \qquad \forall\, i,$$

we can show by using induction and the equations

$$\hat{D}_i^{h+1} = \min_j [d_{ij} + \hat{D}_j^h],$$

$$D_i^{h+1} = \min_j [d_{ij} + D_j^h],$$

$$D_i = \min_j [d_{ij} + D_j],$$

that

$$D_i \leq D_i^h \leq \hat{D}_i^h, \qquad \forall\, i, h.$$

Since $\hat{D}_i^h = D_i$ for $h \geq N - 1$, it follows that $D_i^h = D_i$ for $h \geq N - 1$, proving the desired result.

(b) As stated in the hint, when the length of a link (i, j) on the current shortest path tree increases, the head node i of the link should send an estimated distance $D_i = \infty$ to all nodes m such that (m, i) is a link. These nodes should send $D_m = \infty$ to their upstream neighbors if i is their best neighbor, that is, if link (m, i) lies on the shortest path tree, etc. Before any of the nodes k that sent $D_k = \infty$ to its upstream neighbors recalculates its estimated shortest distance, it should wait for a sufficient amount of time to receive from its downstream neighbors n any updated distances $D_n = \infty$ that may have resulted from the transmission of $D_i = \infty$.

5.7

Using the hint, we begin by showing that $h_i > h_{j_i}$ for all $i \neq 1$. Proof by contradiction. Suppose that there exists some $i \neq 1$ for which $h_i \leq h_{j_i}$. From the Bellman-Ford algorithm we have $D_i^{(h-1)} \geq D_i^{(h)}$. We define $h_1 = 0$ for completeness. Therefore, $D_{j_i}^{(h_i-1)} \geq D_{j_i}^{(h_{j_i})}$. However, if this held with equality it would contradict the definition of h_{j_i} as the largest h such that $D_{j_i}^{(h)} \neq D_{j_i}^{(h-1)}$. Therefore, $D_{j_i}^{(h_i-1)} > D_{j_i}^{(h_{j_i})}$. Using this strict inequality in the definition of j_i, $D_i^{(h_i)} = D_{j_i}^{(h_i-1)} + d_{j_i,i}$, gives $D_i^{(h_i)} > D_{j_i}^{(h_{j_i})} + d_{j_i,i}$. From the Bellman-Ford algorithm, we know that $D_i^{(h_{j_i}+1)} \leq D_{j_i}^{(h_{j_i})} + d_{j_i,i}$. Using this in the previous expression gives $D_i^{(h_i)} > D_i^{(h_{j_i}+1)}$ which contradicts the definition of h_i as the largest h such that $D_i^{(h)} \neq D_i^{(h-1)}$. Therefore, the supposition that $h_i \leq h_{j_i}$ is incorrect. This proves the claim.

The subgraph mentioned in the problem contains $N - 1$ arcs. To show that it is a spanning tree, we must show that it connects every node to node 1. To see this label each node i with h_i. Since the Bellman-Ford algorithm converges in at most $N - 1$ iterations, we have $0 < h_i \leq N - 1$ for all $i \neq 1$. Furthermore, $h_1 = 0$ and $h_i > h_{j_i}$ for all $i \neq 1$. Each node $i \neq 1$ is connected to a neighbor with a smaller label. We can trace a path in the subgraph from every node to node 1, therefore the subgraph must be a spanning tree.

Since the path lengths $D_i^{(h_i)}$ along the subgraph satisfy Bellman's equatation, the spanning tree is a shortest path spanning tree rooted at node 1.

5.8

Bellman's equation is

$$x_i = \min_j \{x_j + d_{ji}\}, \quad i = 2, \ldots, N$$
$$x_1 = 0$$

in the unknown vector $\vec{x}$. One solution is the set of shortest distances d_i from node 1 to each node i. Consider the subgraph G of all arcs (j, i) which are such that $D_i = D_j + dji$.

Claim: Every cycle of zero length not containing node 1 belongs to G.

Proof: If $(i_1, i_2), (i_2, i_3), \ldots, (i_k, i_1)$ is such a zero length cycle, we have

$$0 \le D_{i_1} + d_{i_1 i_2} - D_{i_2}$$
$$0 \le D_{i_2} + d_{i_2 i_3} - D_{i_3}$$
$$\vdots$$
$$0 \le D_{i_k} + d_{i_k i_1} - D_{i_1}.$$

The sum of the right sides is 0, so the right side of each inequality is zero implying that the cycle belongs to G. This proves the claim.

Let C be the set of nodes that participate in a cycle of zero length not containing node 1. Let $\hat{C}$ be the set of nodes i that either belong to C or for which there is a node $j \in C$ and a directed path from j to i in the graph G. Note that $1 \notin \hat{C}$. For any $\delta \ge 0$ let

$$x_i = D_i - \delta \quad \forall\, i \in \hat{C}$$
$$x_i = D_i \qquad \forall\, i \notin \hat{C}.$$

It is easily verified by substitution that the vector $\vec{x}$ defined above is a solution to Bellman's equation.

5.9

Define $S^1 = \{1\}$ and for $k = 1, 2, \ldots$ define

$$S_k = \left\{ \begin{array}{l} \text{all nodes } i \text{ such that either } i \in S_{k-1} \text{ or all} \\ \text{arcs } (j, i) \text{ have their head node } j \text{ in } S_{k-1} \end{array} \right\}$$

Claim: After some index k, S_k equals the entire set of nodes $\mathcal{N}$.

Proof: Let $\bar{S}_k = \mathcal{N} - S_k$ and suppose that S_k is non empty. Take any node $i \in \bar{S}_k$. Then by the connectivity assumption, i will have at least one incoming arc with its head node in S_k. Either all arcs (j, i) have their head node j in S_k, in which case $i \in S_{k+1}$ or else there is a node $j_1 \in \bar{S}_k$ for which (j_1, i) is an arc. In the former case we see that S_{k+1} will be larger than S_k. In the latter case we repeat the process with i replaced by j_1. Eventually, we will obtain a node that belongs to S_{k+1} since otherwise a node in $\bar{S}_k$ would be reencountered thereby closing a directed cycle not containing node 1. This proves that S_{k+1} is larger than S_k. Therefore, S_k will be enlarged if it does not equal $\mathcal{N}$ and for k sufficiently large will equal N. This proves the claim.

Now if m_k is the number of nodes in S_k, renumber the nodes in $S_1 - S_0$ as $2, 3, \ldots, m_1$, then the nodes in $S_2 - S_1$ as $m_1 + 1, \ldots, m_2$ etc. With this numbering each arc (i, j) with $j \neq 1$ is such that $i \in S_{k_1}$ and $j \in S_{k_2} - S_{k_1}$ for some $k_1 < k_2$. The requirement of the problem is satisfied.

If the nodes are renumbered as indicated above, Bellman's equation can be written as

$$
\begin{aligned}
D_i &= \min_{j < i} \{D_j + d_{ji}\}, \quad i = 2, \ldots, N \\
D_1 &= 0
\end{aligned}
$$

and can be solved by successive substitution, i.e., first solve for D_2, then for D_3, etc. This requires at most $O(N^2)$ operations.

5.10

(a) Refer to the algorithm statement in the text. Let B be the lower bound on the arc lengths. Then in step 1, each node $i \notin P$ with

$$
D_i \leq \min_{j \notin P} \{D_j\} + B
$$

can be added to P. To see why this is correct, recall that, at the start of each iteration, D_i for $i \notin P$ is the shortest distance from 1 to i for which all nodes on the path except i lie in P. The inductive argument which proved Dijkstra's algorithm required that each node added to P must have a shortest path for which all but the final node lie in P. This must be true for each node i which meets the above condition, since any path which included another node not in P would have a length of at least D_i.

(b) Assume that the shortest paths from node 1 to all other nodes have been found and have lengths D_j^*, $j \neq 1$. If link (i, k) increases in length, paths which do not traverse link k are not affected by this change. Therefore, we can initialize Dijkstra's algorithm as

$$
P = \left\{ \begin{aligned} &j \text{ such that a shortest path from 1 to } j \\ &\text{does } \textbf{not} \text{ traverse arc } (i, k) \end{aligned} \right\}
$$

$$
\begin{aligned}
D_j &= D_j^* & \text{for all } j \in P \\
D_j &= \min_{l \in P}[D_l + d_{lj}] & \text{for all } j \notin P
\end{aligned}
$$

and continue with the ordinary algorithm.

5.11

(a) We have $D_1 = 0$ throughout the algorithm because initially $D_1 = 0$, and by the rules of the algorithm, D_1 cannot change.

We prove property (1) by induction on the iteration count. Indeed, initially (1) holds, since node 1 is the only node j with $D_j < \infty$. Suppose that (1) holds at the start of some iteration at which a node i is removed from V. If $i = 1$, which happens only at the first iteration, then at the end of the iteration we have $D_j = a_{j1}$ for all inward neighbors j of 1, and $D_j = \infty$ for all other $j \neq 1$, so D_j has the required property. If $j \neq 1$, then $D_j < \infty$ (which is true for all nodes of V by the rules of the algorithm), and (by the induction hypothesis) D_j is the length of some walk P_j starting at j, ending at 1, without going twice through 1. When D_i changes as a result of the iteration, D_i is set to $d_{ij} + D_j$, which is the length of the walk P_i consisting of P_j preceded by arc (i, j). Since $i \neq 1$, P_i does not go twice through 1. This completes the induction proof of property (1).

To prove property (2), note that for any j, each time j is removed from V, the condition $D_i \leq d_{ij} + D_j$ is satisfied for all $(i, j) \in \mathcal{A}$ by the rules of the algorithm. Up to the next entrance of j into V, D_j stays constant, while the labels D_i for all i with $(i, j) \in \mathcal{A}$ cannot increase, thereby preserving the condition $D_i \leq d_{ij} + D_j$.

(b) We first introduce the sets

$$I = \{i \mid D_i < \infty \text{ upon termination}\},$$

$$\overline{I} = \{i \mid d_i = \infty \text{ upon termination}\},$$

and we show that we have $D_j \in \overline{I}$ if and only if there is no walk to 1 from j. Indeed, if $i \in I$, then, since $i \notin V$ upon termination, it follows from condition (2) of part (a) that $j \in I$ for all $(j, i) \in \mathcal{A}$. Therefore, if $j \in \overline{I}$, there is no walk from node j to any node of I (and in particular, node 1). Conversely, if there is no 'walk from j to 1, it follows from condition (1) of part (a) that we cannot have $D_j < \infty$ upon termination, so $j \in \overline{I}$.

We show now that for all $j \in I$, we have $d_j = \min_{(j,i) \in \mathcal{A}} \{d_{ji} + D_i\}$ upon termination. Indeed, conditions (1) and (2) of part (a) imply that upon termination we have, for all $i \in I$,

$$D_j \leq d_{ji} + D_i, \qquad \forall \, j \text{ such that } (j, i) \in \mathcal{A}$$

while D_i is the length of some walk P_i from i to 1. Fix a node $m \in I$. By adding this condition over the arcs (j, i) of any walk P from m to 1, we see that the length of P is no less than D_m. Hence P_m is a shortest walk from m to 1. Furthermore, the equality $D_j = d_{ji} + D_i$ must hold for all arcs (j, i) on the shortest walks P_m, $m \in I$, implying that $D_j = \min_{(j,i) \in \mathcal{A}} \{d_{ji} + D_i\}$.

(c) If the algorithm never terminates, some D_j must decrease strictly an infinite number of times, generating a corresponding sequence of distinct walks P_j as per condition (1) of part (b). Each of these walks can be decomposed into a path from j to 1 plus a collection of cycles. Since the number of paths from j to 1 is finite, and the length of the walk P_j is monotonically decreasing, it follows that P_j eventually must involve a cycle with negative length. By replicating this cycle a sufficiently large number of times, one can obtain walks from j to 1 with arbitrarily small length.

(d) Clear from the statement of Dijkstra's algorithm.

5.12

(a) We first note that the properties of part (a) of Problem 5.11. If upon termination we have $D_t = \infty$, then the extra test $d_{ij} + D_j + u_i < d_t$ for entering V is always passed, so the algorithm generates the same label sequences as the (many destinations) shortest path algorithm of Problem 5.11. Therefore, part(b) of Problem 5.11 applies and shows that there is no path from t to 1.

Let $\overline{D}_j$ be the final value of D_j obtained upon termination and suppose that $\overline{D}_t < \infty$. Assume, to arrive at a contradiction, that there is a path $P_t = (t, j_k, j_{k-1}, \ldots, j_2, j_1, t)$ that has length L_t with $L_t < \overline{D}_t$. For $m = 1, \ldots, k$, let L_{j_m} be the length of the path $P_m = (j_m, j_{m-1}, \ldots, j_2, j_1, t)$.

Let us focus on the node j_k following t on the path P_t. We claim that $L_{j_k} < \overline{D}_{j_k}$. Indeed, if this were not so, then j_k must have been removed at some iteration from V with D_{j_k} satisfying $D_{j_k} \leq L_{j_k}$. If D_t is the estimate of t at the start of that iteration, we would then have

$$d_{tj_k} + D_{j_k} \leq d_{tj_k} + L_{j_k} = L_t < \overline{D}_t \leq D_t,$$

implying that the shortest distance estimate of t would be reduced at that iteration from D_t to $d_{tj_k} + D_{j_k}$, which is less than the final estimate $\overline{D}_t$ – a contradiction.

Next we focus on the node j_{k-1} following j_k and t on the path P_t. We use a similar (though not identical) argument to show that $L_{j_{k-1}} < \overline{D}_{j_{k-1}}$. Indeed, if this were not so, then j_{k-1} must have been removed at some iteration from V with $D_{j_{k-1}}$ satisfying $D_{j_{k-1}} \leq L_{j_{k-1}}$. If D_{j_k} and D_t are the shortest distance estimates of j_k and t at the start of that iteration, we would then have

$$d_{j_k j_{k-1}} + D_{j_{k-1}} \leq d_{j_k j_{k-1}} + L_{j_{k-1}} = L_{j_k} < \overline{D}_{j_k} \leq D_{j_k},$$

and since $L_{j_k} + u_{j_k} \leq L_t < \overline{D}_t \leq D_t$, we would also have

$$d_{j_k j_{k-1}} + D_{j_{k-1}} < D_t - u_{j_k}.$$

From the above two equations, it follows that the shortest distance estimate of j_k would be reduced at that iteration from D_{j_k} to $d_{tj_k} + D_{j_k}$, which is less than the final label $\overline{D}_{j_k}$ – a contradiction.

Proceeding similarly, we obtain $L_{j_m} < \overline{D}_{j_m}$ for all $m = 1, \ldots, k$, and in particular $d_{j_1 1} = L_{j_1} < \overline{D}_{j_1}$. Since

$$d_{j_1 1} + u_{j_1} \le L_t < \overline{D}_t,$$

and D_t is monotonically nonincreasing throughout the algorithm, we see that at the first iteration, j_1 will enter V with the label $a_{j_1 1}$, which cannot be less than the final estimate $\overline{D}_{j_1}$. This is a contradiction; the proof of part (b) is complete.

(b) The proof is identical to the proof of Problem 5.11(c).

5.13

Suppose that the sequence number field is finite with maximum equal to M. The exceptional circumstances referred to in the problem statement arise when the sequence number for updates of some node i becomes M within the memory of some other node, say j, due to a memory or communication error. Then the next time node i floods a new update into the network, it will receive M from node j through the feedback mechanism described at the end of section 5.3.2. The question now is how node i can convince node j to reduce its stored sequence number so that it can listen to a new update from node i.

The remedy is for node i, once it detects an error of the type described above, to issue a special "reset" packet which is flooded through the network. A node receiving a reset packet originated at node i sets its stored sequence number for node i to zero, and sends the reset packet to all its neighbors except the one from which the reset packet was received. In this way all nodes connected with node i will reset their sequence numbers to zero and the wraparound condition will be corrected.

There are two issues here: first how to avoid indefinite circulation of reset packets, and second how to guarantee that reset packets will not interfere with regular update packets or other reset packets from the same node. A clean way to ensure this (even if the links can reverse the order of reception of packets) is to add an age field to a reset packet which makes it "live" for exactly A seconds. The age limit A should be larger than the known upper bound for the time required for the reset packet to reach all nodes, so that the reset packet will live long enough to reset the sequence numbers of all nodes to zero. To avoid confusion node i should not issue any other update or reset packet for A seconds after issuing a reset packet. Finally, unlimited circulation of a reset packet, and confusion with other packets from node i, are avoided by requiring a node $j \neq i$ not to accept a reset packet or any update packet issued by node i if node j has received a reset packet from node i which is still "live." This is so because update packets from node i issued before the reset packet was issued cannot arrive at another node after the reset packet's age has expired under the assumption that an update packet reaches all nodes in time less than A. Note that this protocol could be used to operate flooding with a relatively small sequence number field. On the other hand, knowing an upper bound on the time required for an update packet to reach all nodes is a strong assumption, and one would like to minimize reliance on it.

5.14

A node is considered adjacent to the directed links for which it is the head node. Each node i decides upon a value associated with each of its adjacent links. We wish to find an algorithm which will reliably broadcast these values to each network node. To accomplish this we augment the SPTA as follows.

In addition to the main and port topology tables, let each node i keep similarly organized main and port information tables (Γ^i and Γ^i_j respectively) which contain entries for each directed link. The communication rules for these tables are the same as for the topology tables. When an entry for a non-adjacent link (m,n) changes in one of node i's port information tables, it updates the corresponding entry in its main table by setting

$$\Gamma^i(m,n) = \Gamma^i_{L(m)}(m,n),$$

where $L(m)$ is the label for node m which was assigned by the main topology table update algorithm. When the labels $L(m)$ are updated due to a topology change, each entry in Γ^i for a non adjacent link must be updated in this manner.

The value of $\Gamma^i(m,n)$ can be easily proven to be correct at each node i by using the fact that $L(m)$ at node i is the first hop on a shortest hop path from i to m. We first show that it is correct for nodes i which are 1 hop from m, then 2 hops etc.

5.15

(a)   The algorithm can fail in the network shown below.

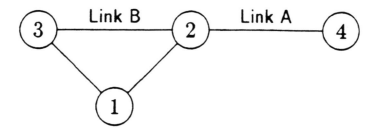

The table below shows a sequence of link status changes and message exchanges which lead the algorithm to fail. These events have been divided into numbered sections for reference purposes. The notation "$(i \rightarrow j, l\downarrow)$" is used to indicate that node i sends a message to node j indicating that link l is down. The entries in the topology column give the perceived status of link A at nodes 1 through 4 respectively. All links are initially up. We are only interested how the nodes determine the status of link A; messages concerning link B are not shown.

#	Description	Topology
1	Link A fails. $(2\rightarrow1, A\downarrow)$ sent and received. $(2\rightarrow3, A\downarrow)$ send and received.	dddd
2	Link B fails. $(1\rightarrow3, A\downarrow)$ sent and received. $(3\rightarrow1, A\downarrow)$ sent.	dddd
3	Link A is repaired. $(2\rightarrow1, A\uparrow)$ sent and received.	uudu
4	$(3\rightarrow1, A\downarrow)$ from #2 is received. $(1\rightarrow3, A\uparrow)$ sent and received.	duuu
5	Link A fails. $(1\rightarrow2, A\downarrow)$ sent and received. $(2\rightarrow1, A\downarrow)$ sent and received.	ddud

After #5, the algorithm terminates with node 3 having an incorrect status for link A.

(b)   We use the same scenario as in part (a) up to #4. The extra messages sent, due to the "including" rule, have no effect on the topology up to this point. The table below shows a scenario illustrating failure of the algorithm.

#	Description	Topology
4	$(1{\rightarrow}3, A{\uparrow})$ sent and received. $(1{\rightarrow}2, A{\uparrow})$ sent and received. $(3{\rightarrow}1, A{\downarrow})$ from #2 is received.	duuu
5	$(3{\rightarrow}1, A{\uparrow})$ sent and received. $(1{\rightarrow}2, A{\downarrow})$ sent and received. $(1{\rightarrow}3, A{\downarrow})$ sent and received.	uudu
6	$(2{\rightarrow}1, A{\uparrow})$ sent and received first. $(3{\rightarrow}1, A{\downarrow})$ sent and received second. $(1{\rightarrow}3, A{\uparrow})$ sent and received. $(1{\rightarrow}2, A{\uparrow})$ sent and received.	duuu
7	Same as #5.	uudu

Nodes 1 and 3 can oscillate indefinitely concerning their opinion of link A's status, and the algorithm never terminates. Although node 2 has the correct information, unfortunate message timing can stop it from helping the situation. This failure mode is at least as serious as that in part (a).

5.16

The ARPANET and the other algorithms which use sequence numbers are not affected. The sequence numbers can be used to sort out the correct message order. However, SPTA is clearly affected by a change in message order. For example, suppose that a link goes down and then up. If the adjacent nodes reverse the order of the two messages, the algorithm will fail to arrive at the correct topology.

5.17

(a)   In the algorithm that follows, each node has two possible states, "connected" or "not connected". In addition, each node marks each of its neighbors with one of the following: "unknown", "not in tree", "incoming", or "outgoing". There are two kinds of messages used: "attach" and "ack". The following are the procedures executed at each node i.

<u>Initially at each node i</u>
state = "not connected"
mark(j) = "unknown" for each neighbor j

<u>Start (Node 1 only)</u>
state = "connected"
send "attach" to each neighbor

Receive "attach" from j
_____
if state = "not connected"
  then state = "connected"
      mark(j) = "outgoing"
      if node i has neighbors other than j
        then send "attach" to each neighbor except j
        else send "ack" to j
            end
  else mark(j) = "not in tree"
      if mark$(k) \neq$ "unknown" for each neighbor k
        then send "ack" to the neighbor k such that mark(k) = "outgoing"†
           end

Receive "ack" from j
_____
mark(j) = "incoming"
if mark$(k) \neq$ "unknown" for each neighbor k
  then send "ack" to the neighbor k such that mark(k) = "outgoing"†
      end
†Node 1 just terminates the algorithm; it has no "outgoing" neighbor

The above algorithm sends one "attach" and one "ack" message on each spanning tree link, and sends two "attach" messages (one in each direction) on each link not in the tree. Therefore, it sends a total of $2A$ messages.

(b) We use the spanning tree constructed in part (a) to simplify counting the nodes. Each node marks its "incoming" neighbors with either "heard from" or "not heard from". There are two messages used: "count nodes", and a messages containing a single number $j : 0 < j < N$. The following is the procedure for each node i.

Initialization
_____
mark(j) = "not heard from" for all "incoming" neighbors
children = 0

Start (node 1 only)
_____
send "count nodes" to all "incoming" neighbors

Receive "count nodes" from "outgoing" neighbor j
_____
if there are any "incoming" neighbors
  then send "count nodes" on all incoming links
  else send "1" to j
      end

Receive n from "incoming" neighbor j
_____
children = children + n

mark(j) = "heard from"
if mark(k) = "heard from" for all "incoming" neighbors k
   then send (children + 1) to the "outgoing" neighbor†
         end

†Node 1 has no outgoing neighbor. When it reaches this step, N = children + 1.

(c)   The worst case for both algorithms is a linear network. Messages must propagate from node 1 to the end of the tree and then back again. This gives an upper bound of $2(N-1)T$ for both algorithms.

5.18

In the algorithm, for $j \notin P$, D_j is the minimum 1 hop distance from j to a member of P, and a_j is the member of P for which this minimum is obtained.

To show that this implements the Prim-Dijkstra algorithm, we must show that the graph defined by $G = (P, T)$ is a fragment of an MST, and that this fragment is enlarged at each iteration by the addition of a minimum weight outgoing arc. Then, by Proposition 1 in section 2.2, G will eventually be an MST.

Assume that P contains k nodes, that a_j is the closest member of P to j, and that $D_j = w_{ja_j}$ for $j \notin P$. Then step 1 chooses the minimum weight outgoing arc, and step 2 reestablishes the above assumptions about a_j and D_j for the new set P. The hypothesis is clearly true for $k = 1$ and by induction is true for all k.

Each iteration of steps 1 and 2 requires a number of operations proportional to the number of nodes $i : i \notin P$. The algorithm terminates in $N - 1$ iterations. Therefore, $O(N^2)$ operations are required.

5.19

Choose n_1, n_1, n_2 as shown below

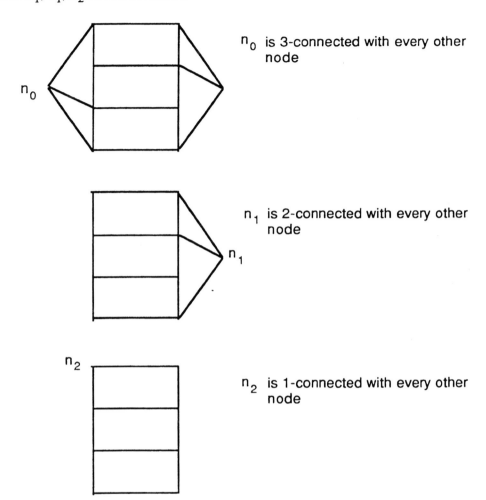

n_0 is 3-connected with every other node

n_1 is 2-connected with every other node

n_2 is 1-connected with every other node

The network is not 4 - connected as shown below. (Removal of nodes n_0, n_1, and n_2 leaves node n_3 disconnected from the others.) The maximum k for which the network is k - connected is k = 3.

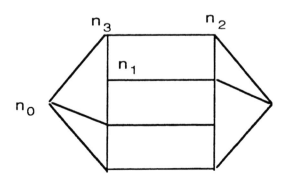

5.20

Modification of Kleitman's algorithm:

1st Step:

Choose a node n_0 and let k_0 be the maximum number k for which n_0 is k - connected to all other nodes. Set k' = k_0. If k_0 = 1 terminate, else delete n_0 and its adjacent arcs.

(m+1)st Step:

Choose a node n_m and let k_m be the maximum number k for which n_m is k - connected to all other nodes. Set $k' := \min\{k', k_m + m\}$. If $k_m \leq 1$ terminate, else delete n_m and its adjacent arcs and go to the (m + 2)nd step.

Claim: At termination the desired maximum number is k'.

Proof: The network cannot be k" - connected with k" > k' because the construction of k' is such that Kleitman's test of k" - connectedness for the sequence of nodes $n_0, n_1, \ldots,$ would fail. Also the algorithm will eventually terminate, and we will have $k_m \leq k'$ - m for every m. It follows that Kleitman's test of k' - connectivity is passed.

Application of the modified algorithm to the graph of Problem 5.19 works as follows:

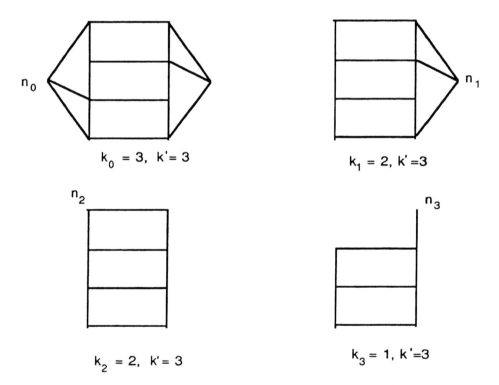

k_0 = 3, k'= 3 k_1 = 2, k' =3

k_2 = 2, k' = 3 k_3 = 1, k'=3

5.21

The sequence of generated spanning trees is shown below:

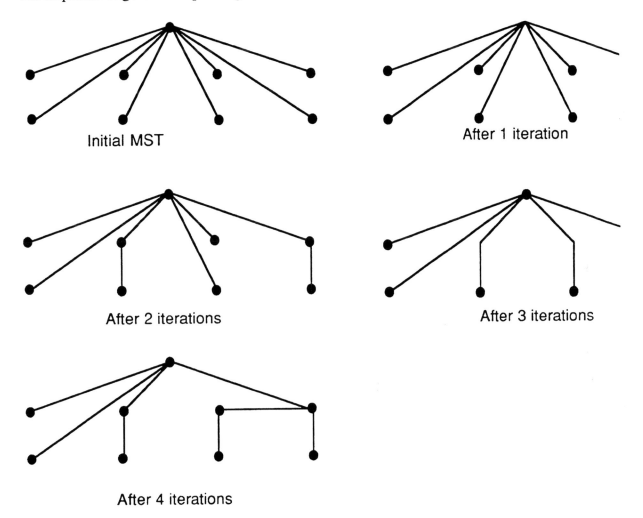

Initial MST

After 1 iteration

After 2 iterations

After 3 iterations

After 4 iterations

5.22

(a) Suppose every i to j walk contains an arc with weight greater or equal to a_{ij}. Consider an MST and the (unique) walk from i to j on the MST. If this walk does not consist of just arc (i,j), then replace an arc of this walk with weight greater or equal to a_{ij} with arc (i,j), thereby obtaining an MST.

Conversely suppose to obtain a contradiction, that (i,j) belongs to an MST and that there exists a walk W from i to j with all arcs having weight smaller than a_{ij}. We remove (i,j) from the MST obtaining two subtrees T_i and T_j containing i and j, respectively. The walk W must contain an arc that connects a node of T_i to a node of T_j. Adding that arc to the two subtrees T_i and T_j creates a spanning tree with smaller weight than that of the original, which is a contradiction.

(b) Walks from i to j that use nodes 1 through k+1 are of two types: 1) walks that use only nodes 1 through k or 2) walks that go from i to k+1 using nodes 1 through k and then from k+1 to j using nodes 1 through k. The minimum critical weight of walks of type 1) is x_{ij}^k, while the critical weight over walks of type 2) is $\max\{x_{i(k+1)}^k, x_{(k+1)j}^k\}$. The characterization of x_{ij}^k given in the exercise follows.

5.23

(a) Let T^* be the given tree that spans the given subset of nodes and has minimal total weight W^*. Let T be a minimum weight spanning tree of I(G) and let W be its total weight. Finally, let R be a minimum weight tour of I(G) and let Y be its total weight.

By deleting any arc of R we obtain a spanning tree R' of I(G), which must have weight no more than the weight Y of R (since arc weights are nonnegative), and no less than the weight W of T [since T is a minimum weight spanning tree of I(G)]. Therefore

$$W \leq Y \tag{1}$$

We will also show that

$$Y \leq 2W^* \tag{2}$$

so that from (1) and (2), the desired result

$$W \leq 2W^*$$

follows.

By selecting an arbitrary node r of T^* as root we can view T^* as a tree rooted at r. Consider a depth-first traversal of T^* as illustrated in the following figure.

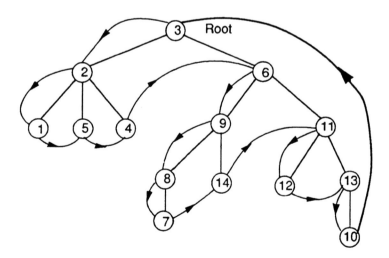

Traversal Order: 3, 2, 1, 5, 4, 6, 9, 8, 7, 14, 11, 12, 13, 10, 3

This traversal corresponds to a tour R' of I(G). Each arc (i,j) of the tour has length which is less than or equal to the length of the unique path of T^* that connects i and j. The lengths of all these paths add up to $2W^*$, as can be seen from the figure. Therefore, the length Y' of the tour is no more than $2W^*$. Since Y is the weight of the minimum weight tour, we have $Y \le Y'$, so it follows that $Y \le 2W^*$.

(b) Consider the following grpah G with the weights shown next to the arcs, and let {1,2,3} be the subset of nodes that must be spanned by T^*.

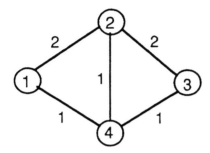

The graph I(G) is shown below together with the corresponding arc weights.

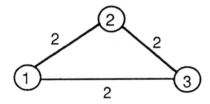

We have $T^* = \{(1,4), (2,4), (3,4)\}$ with total weight $W^* = 3$. On the other hand $T = \{(1,2), (2,3)\}$ and $W = 4$, so that

$$W^* < W < 2W^*$$

(c) Construct the minimum spanning tree T of I(G). For each arc (i,j) of T, consider a shortest path of G that starts at i and ends at j. Consider the subgraph G' of G that consists of the arcs of all the shortest paths corresponding to all the arcs of T. The sum of the weights of the arcs of G' is no more than the total weight W of T (it could be less because some arc of G' may be contained in more than one shortest path). Clearly G' is connected. Delete as many arcs as necessary to make it a tree. This tree, call it T', spans the required nodes and has total weight that is less or equal to W and therefore also less or equal to $2W^*$. Thus, the broadcasting algorithm that uses T' comes within a factor of 2 of being optimal.

5.24

See the hint.

5.25

If x_i is the flow carried by link i (i = 1, 2, 3), the corresponding path lengths are $C_i/(C_i-$

$x_i)^2$. At an optimum x_1 and x_3 must be equal since if, for example, $x_1 > x_3$ we will have that the length of x_1 is larger than the length of path 1 is larger than that of path 3 which contradicts the shortest path optimality condition.

Let x be the common value of x_1 and x_3 at the optimum. Then $x_2 = r - 2x$ and the solution of the problem follows the lines of the example of Section 5.5. We argue that, because $C_2 > C$, the only two possibilities are:

1) $x_2 = 0$ and $x = r/2$, which will occur for

$$C/(C - r/2)^2 \leq 1/C_2$$

2) $x_2 > 0$, and $x = (r - x_2)/2 > 0$ in which case x_2 and x are determined using the condition

$$C/(C - r/2 + x_2/2)^2 = C_2/(C_2 - x_2)^2.$$

5.26

(a) We have at x^*

$$\partial D(x^*)/\partial x_1 = x_1^* = 2/3, \quad \partial D(x^*)/\partial x_2 = 2x_2^* = 2/3, \quad \partial D(x^*)/\partial x_3 = 1 + x_3^* = 1.$$

Therefore x^* satisfies the shortest path condition and is optimal.

5.27

a) If the cost function is $D(x)$ where x is the path flow vector, the first derivatives become

$$\frac{\partial D(x)}{\partial x_p} = \sum_{(i,j)} \frac{\partial D_{ij}(x)}{\partial x_p}.$$

A shortest path for a given OD pair is a path with minimal first derivative over all paths of the OD pair. The first derivatives of the reduced cost $D^r(x)$, i.e. the cost function obtained after the flows of the shortest paths are expressed in terms of the flows of the nonshortest paths in the cost function $D(x)$, are given by

$$\frac{\partial D^r(x)}{\partial x_p} = \frac{\partial D(x)}{\partial x_p} - \frac{\partial D(x)}{\partial x_{p_w}}, \qquad \text{for all } p \in P_w$$

where p_w is the path from P_w that is shortest (has smallest $\partial D/\partial x_p$). The second derivatives are

$$\frac{\partial^2 D^r(x)}{(\partial x_p)^2} = \frac{\partial^2 D(x)}{(\partial x_p)^2} + \frac{\partial^2 D(x)}{(\partial x_{p_w})^2} - 2\frac{\partial^2 D(x)}{\partial x_p \partial x_{p_w}} .$$

The iteration for nonshortest paths becomes

$$x_p := \max\{0, x_p - [\frac{\partial^2 D^r(x)}{(\partial x_p)^2}]^{-1} \frac{\partial D^r(x)}{\partial x_p} \}.$$

The optimality condition is the same as in Section 5.5 (cf. eq. (5.59)).

b) In the special case where

$$D(x) = \sum_{(i,j)} D_{ij}(\tilde{F}_{ij}, F_{ij})$$

we have for a path p of priority class k

$$\frac{\partial D(x)}{\partial x_p} = \sum_{(i,j) \text{ on path } p} (p_k \frac{\partial D_{ij}}{\partial \tilde{F}_{ij}} + \frac{\partial D_{ij}}{\partial F_{ij}})$$

$$\frac{\partial^2 D(x)}{(\partial x_p)^2} = \sum_{(i,j) \text{ on path } p} (p_k^2 \frac{\partial^2 D_{ij}}{(\partial \tilde{F}_{ij})^2} + 2p_k \frac{\partial^2 D_{ij}}{\partial \tilde{F}_{ij} \partial F_{ij}} + \frac{\partial^2 D_{ij}}{(\partial F_{ij})^2})$$

and from here everything is the same as in part a).

5.28

The key in this problem is to calculate the 1st derivatives of the cost with respect to the portion x_t of R broadcast on any one spanning tree $t \in T$. We have:

$$\frac{\partial D}{\partial x_t} = \sum_{(i,j) \text{ on } t} D_{ij}' ,$$

as well as the constraint $\Sigma_{t \in T} x_t = R$. By the same argument used in Section 5.5, this leads to the following necessary and sufficient optimality condition (in addition to the ones of Section 5.5 for ordinary paths)

$x_t^* > 0 \quad \Rightarrow \quad$ t is shortest in that it has minimum $\Sigma_{(i,j) \in t} D_{ij}^{\cdot}$ over all trees in T.

(This means that at an optimum only the trees with minimum $\sum_{(i,j) \in t} D_{ij}'$ can carry a portion of R. Those that do must, of course, have equal $\sum_{(i,j) \in t} D_{ij}'$.) Given these facts, the gradient projection method generalizes easily. The iteration for flows on trees is the same as that for paths with the derivative $\sum_{(i,j) \in t} D_{ij}'$ for a tree t used in place of the 1st derivative length of a path flow. Similarly the case of multiple root nodes is a straightforward extension. The optimality conditions and gradient projection iterations for different roots are decoupled.

5.29

The length of a path is

$$\frac{\partial D}{\partial x_p} = \sum_{(i,j) \text{ on } p} (D_{ij}' + c_{ww'} D_{ji}').$$

The optimality condition is

$$x_p^* > 0 \quad \Rightarrow \quad \text{p is shortest over all paths of the same OD pair with respect to length of link (i,j)} = D_{ij}' + c_{ww'} D_{ji}'.$$

The extension of the gradient projection method is straightforward using the expression for path lengths given above.

5.30

For simplicity we drop the subscripts. Let $Q(F) = a + bF + 0.5\,cF^2$ be the quadratic function where a, b, c are its unknown coefficients. Denote $D(F) = F/(C - F)$. The derivatives are

$$D'(F) = C/(C - F)^2, \quad D''(F) = 2C/(C - F)^3$$

and

$$Q'(F) = b + cF, \qquad Q''(F) = c.$$

We determine a, b, c via the condition that D and its derivatives should equal Q and its corresponding derivatives at $F = \rho C$. This leads to the equations

$$c = 2/(1 - \rho)^3 C^2$$

$$b + \rho c C = 1/(1 - \rho)^2 C$$

$$a + \rho b C + 0.5\,\rho^2 c C^2/2 = \rho/(1 - \rho),$$

which can be easily solved to give the values of a, b, c. D(F) is then replaced by the function

$$\tilde{D}(F)$$

which equals D(F) for F ≤ ρC and equals Q(F) otherwise.

The last assertion of the problem follows from the fact that the necessary condition for the F_{ij}^* to minimize

$$\sum_{(i,j)} D_{ij}(F_{ij})$$

(i.e. the shortest path condition of Section 5.5) is also a sufficient condition for minimizing

$$\sum_{(i,j)} \tilde{D}_{ij}(F_{ij})$$

when $F_{ij} \le \rho_{ij}C_{ij}$ for all (i,j).

5.31

(a) For every x and y we have (by Taylor's theorem)

$$\int_0^1 \nabla f(x + ty)'y\,dt = f(x + y) - f(x)$$

so by applying this formula for $y = \alpha \Delta x$ we obtain

$$f(x + \alpha \Delta x) = f(x) + \nabla f(x)'(\alpha \Delta x) + \int_0^1 [\nabla f(x + t\alpha \Delta x) - \nabla f(x)]'(\alpha \Delta x)\,dt$$

$$\le f(x) + \alpha \nabla f(x)'\Delta x + \alpha \int_0^1 |\nabla f(x + t\alpha \Delta x) - \nabla f(x)|\,|\Delta x|\,dt$$

$$\le f(x) + \alpha \nabla f(x)'\Delta x + \frac{\alpha^2 L}{2}|\Delta x|^2 \qquad (1)$$

which is the desired relation.

(b) Minimizing both sides of (1) over $\alpha \in [0, 1]$ we obtain

$$\min_{\alpha \in [0,1]} f(x + \alpha \Delta x) \leq f(x) + \min_{\alpha \in [0,1]} \{\alpha \nabla f(x)' \Delta x + \frac{\alpha^2 L}{2} |\Delta x|^2\} \qquad (2)$$

Since $\nabla f(x)' \Delta x < 0$ the minimum on the right is attained for some $\alpha' > 0$. The unconstrained minimum is attained at the scalar α^* for which the derivative $\nabla f(x)' \Delta x + \alpha^* L |\Delta x|^2$ is zero or

$$\alpha^* = -\frac{\nabla f(x)' \Delta x}{L |\Delta x|^2} .$$

If $\alpha^* \geq 1$ or $\nabla f(x)' \Delta x + L |\Delta x|^2 < 0$ the minimum on the right side of (2) is attained for $\alpha'=1$, and we obtain

$$\min_{\alpha \in [0,1]} f(x + \alpha \Delta x) \leq f(x) + \nabla f(x)' \Delta x + \frac{L}{2} |\Delta x|^2 \leq \nabla f(x) + \frac{\nabla f(x)' \Delta x}{2} \qquad (3)$$

where the last inequality follows from the relation $\nabla f(x)' \Delta x + L |\Delta x|^2 < 0$.

If $\alpha^* < 1$ then the minimum over $[0, 1]$ is attained for $\alpha' = \alpha^*$ and substitution in (2) yields

$$\min_{\alpha \in [0,1]} f(x + \alpha \Delta x) \leq f(x) - \frac{|\nabla f(x)' \Delta x|^2}{L |\Delta x|^2} + \frac{|\nabla f(x)' \Delta x|^2}{L^2 |\Delta x|^4} \frac{L |\Delta x|^2}{2}$$

$$= f(x) - \frac{|\nabla f(x)' \Delta x|^2}{2L |\Delta x|^2} \leq f(x) - \frac{|\nabla f(x)' \Delta x|^2}{2LR^2} .$$

c) If $\{x^k\}$ has a limit point x^*, then since $\{f(x^k)\}$ is monotonically decreasing, we must have $f(x^k) \to f(x^*)$ which implies $\delta^k \to 0$. Therefore $\nabla f(x^k)' \Delta x^k \to 0$, and the result follows as stated in the hint.

5.32

(a) Applying the necessary condition for the projection problem with $x = x^k$ we obtain

$$s \nabla f(x^k)'(\bar{x}^k - x^k) \leq -|\bar{x}^k - x^k|^2 \qquad (1)$$

Using the conclusion of part b) of Problem 5.31 we obtain

$$\min_{\alpha \in [0,1]} f(x^k + s\Delta x^k) \le f(x^k) + \delta^k$$

where

$$\Delta x^k = \bar{x}^k - x^k$$

and where, [using also (1)],

$$\delta^k \le -\frac{|\Delta x^k|^2}{2s} \qquad \text{if} \quad \nabla f(x^k)'\Delta x^k + L\,|\Delta x^k|^2 < 0$$

$$\delta^k \le -\frac{|\Delta x^k|^4}{2s^2 L R^2} \qquad \text{otherwise}$$

Therefore if $\{x^k\}$ has a limit point x^* we must have $f(x^k) \to f(x^*)$ and $\delta^k \to 0$. Therefore   .

$$\Delta x^k \to 0, \qquad \{\bar{x}^k\} \to x^* ,$$

and by taking limit in the condition

$$[x^k - s\nabla f(x^k) - \bar{x}^k]'\,(x - \bar{x}^k) \le 0$$

for all $x \in X$ we obtain $\nabla f(x^*)'(x - x^*) \ge 0$ for all $x \in X$.

(b) Using (1) and part a) of Problem 5.31 we obtain (for $\alpha = 1$)

$$f(x^{k+1}) \le f(x^k) + \nabla f(x^k)'\Delta x^k + \frac{L}{2}\,|\Delta x^k|^2$$

$$\le f(x^k) - \frac{|\Delta x^k|^2}{s} + \frac{L}{2}\,|\Delta x^k|^2$$

$$= f(x^k) - (\frac{1}{s} - \frac{L}{2})\,|\Delta x^k|^2$$

If $s < 2/L$ then the cost is reduced by at least a positive constant multiple of $|\Delta x^k|^2$ at the kth iteration. The result follows similarly as for part a).

5.33

Consider the change of variables $y = T^{-1}x$ or $x = Ty$. Then the problem can be written in terms of the y variables as

$$\text{min } f(Ty)$$
$$\text{subject to } Ty \geq 0$$

or equivalently, because T is diagonal with positive diagonal elements,

$$\text{min } h(y)$$
$$\text{subject to } y \geq 0$$

The second iteration in the problem is the gradient projection iteration for the second problem above. We have

$$\frac{\partial h(y)}{\partial y_i} = \sqrt{b_i} \frac{\partial f(x)}{\partial x_i}$$

Substituting this expression in the second iteration and multiplying throughout by $\sqrt{b_i}$ we obtain the first iteration of the problem. So the diagonally scaled version of the gradient projection iteration is the same as the ordinary version applied to a problem involving the diagonally scaled variables y_i.

5.34

(a) Since an arrival comes every τ time units, the system starts empty, and each arrival stays for H time units, we see that just after time $H-\tau$ there will be a total of H/τ arrivals. The first departure occurs at time H and at the same time an arrival occurs, which maintains the total number $N_1(t) + N_2(t)$ in the system at the level H/τ. Similarly, this number is maintained for all t.

(b) We first calculate N_1^* and N_2^*. The optimality condition is that the partial cost derivatives with respect to N_1 and N_2 are equal, so we have

$$\gamma_1 N_1^* = \gamma_2 N_2^*.$$

By combining this equation with the constraint

$$N_1^* + N_1^* = \frac{H}{\tau}, \tag{1}$$

we obtain

$$N_1^* = \frac{\gamma_2}{\gamma_1 + \gamma_2} \frac{H}{\tau}, \quad N_2^* = \frac{\gamma_1}{\gamma_1 + \gamma_2} \frac{H}{\tau}.$$

Define for all t

$$N(t) = N_1(t) + N_2(t), \tag{2}$$

$$N_1^*(t) = \frac{\gamma_2}{\gamma_1 + \gamma_2} N(t),$$

(3)

$$N_2^*(t) = \frac{\gamma_1}{\gamma_1 + \gamma_2} N(t),$$

(4)

and note that for $t > H$ we have

$$N(t) = N_1^* + N_2^* = \frac{H}{\tau}, \quad N_1^*(t) = N_1^*, N_2^*(t) = N_2^*.$$

(5)

The relation

$$\gamma_1 N_1(t) \le \gamma_2 N_2(t)$$

is equivalent to

$$\gamma_1 N_1(t) \le \gamma_2 (N(t) - N_1(t))$$

or

$$N_1(t) \le \frac{\gamma_2}{\gamma_1 + \gamma_2} N(t) = N_1^*(t),$$

where the last equation follows by using Eq. (3). Thus, we have

$$\gamma_1 N_1(t) \le \gamma_2 N_2(t) \iff N_1(t) \le N_1^*(t),$$

(6)

and similarly

$$\gamma_2 N_2(t) \le \gamma_1 N_1(t) \iff N_2(t) \le N_2^*(t).$$

(7)

We will now prove by induction that all $k = 0,1,...,$ and all $t \in [kT, (k+1)T)$, we have

$$\frac{N_1(t) - N_1^*(kT)}{N_1^*} \le \frac{\gamma_1 + \gamma_2}{\gamma_1} \frac{T}{H},$$

(8)

$$\frac{N_2(t) - N_2^*(kT)}{N_2^*} \le \frac{\gamma_1 + \gamma_2}{\gamma_1} \frac{T}{H}.$$

(9)

We claim that these relations are true for $k = 0$. Indeed we have

$$N_1^*(0) = N_1(0) = N_2(0) = 0,$$

so by the rules of the algorithm, all VCs arriving in the interval $[0,T]$ will be assigned to link 1. Since the number of these VCs is at most T/τ, we have

$$N_1(t) \leq N_1^*(0) + \frac{T}{\tau}.$$

(10)

By using Eq. (1), we see that

$$\frac{T}{\tau} = \frac{\gamma_1 + \gamma_2}{\gamma_2} \frac{T}{H} N_1^*,$$

so Eq. (10) yields

$$\frac{N_1(t) - N_1^*(0)}{N_1^*} \leq \frac{\gamma_1 + \gamma_2}{\gamma_2} \frac{T}{H},$$

thus verifying Eq. (8) for k=0. Eq. (9) holds for k=0 since $N_2^*(t) = 0$.

We will now show that Eqs. (8) and (9) hold for the typical k, assuming they hold for all preceding k.

We assume without loss of generality that $\gamma_1 N_1(kT) \leq \gamma_2 N_2(kT)$ or equivalently by Eq. (6),

$$N_1(kT) \leq N_1^*(kT).$$

(11)

Then by the rules of the algorithm, all VCs arriving in the interval [kT, (k+1)T) will be assigned to link 1. Since the number of these VC's is at most T/t, we have

$$N_1(t) \leq N_1^*(kT) + \frac{T}{\tau}, \quad \forall t \in [kT, (k+1)T).$$

(12)

By using Eq. (1), we see that

$$\frac{T}{\tau} = \frac{\gamma_1 + \gamma_1}{\gamma_2} \frac{T}{H} N_1^*,$$

so Eq. (12) yields

$$\frac{N_1(t) - N_1^*(kT)}{N_1^*} \leq \frac{\gamma_1 + \gamma_2}{\gamma_2} \frac{T}{H},$$

(13)

proving Eq. (8) for the typical k.

In view of Eq. (11), we also have

$$N_2(kT) \geq N_2^*(kT)$$

as well as

$$N_2(t) \leq N_2(kT), \quad \forall t \in [kT, (k+1)T).$$

Therefore we have

$$N_2(T) - N_2^*(kT) \geq N_2(t) - N_2^*(kT), \quad \forall\, t \in [kT, (k+1)T)$$

and Eq. (9) holds in view of the induction hypothesis. Thus the induction proof of Eqs. (8) and (9) is complete.

From Eqs. (8) and (9), since $N_1^*(t) = N_1^*$, $N_2^*(t) = N_2^*$ for $t > H$, we have for all $t > H$

$$\frac{N_1(t) - N_1^*}{N_1^*} \leq \frac{\gamma_1 + \gamma_2}{\gamma_2}\frac{T}{H}, \tag{14}$$

$$\frac{N_2(t) - N_2^*}{N_2^*} \leq \frac{\gamma_1 + \gamma_2}{\gamma_1}\frac{T}{H}. \tag{15}$$

Since $N_1(t) - N_1^* = N_2 = N_2(t)$, from Eq. (14) we obtain

$$N_2^* - N_2(t) \leq \frac{\gamma_1 + \gamma_2}{\gamma_2}\frac{T}{H}N_1^* = \frac{\gamma_1 + \gamma_2}{\gamma_1}\frac{T}{H}N_2^*$$

or equivalently

$$\frac{N_2^* - N_2(t)}{N_2^*} \leq \frac{\gamma_1 + \gamma_2}{\gamma_1}\frac{T}{H}.$$

Combining this relation with Eq. (15), we obtain

$$\frac{|N_2(t) - N_2^*|}{N_2^*} \leq \frac{\gamma_1 + \gamma_2}{\gamma_1}\frac{T}{H},$$

and we similarly prove the remaining relation

$$\frac{|N_1(t) - N_1^*|}{N_1^*} \leq \frac{\gamma_1 + \gamma_2}{\gamma_2}\frac{T}{H}.$$

5.35

To make the protocol workable it is essential to number sequentially the exploratory packets. (This is needed, for example, in order to avoid confusion between transmitter and receiver regarding two distinct VC setup requests. There are also other reasons for this as will be seen shortly.) There should be a separate sequence number for each origin - destination (OD) pair, and it will be assumed that the sequence number field is so large that wraparound never occurs in the absence of memory or transmission errors.

Indefinite circulation can be avoided if each node relays a received exploratory packet only to neghbor nodes not yet visited by the packet (i.e., the nodes that are not stamped on the packet). This rule guarantees that the exploratory packet will travel on all possible routes from origin to destination that contain no loops. Thus the destination will receive one copy of the exploratory packet for each distinct route that was up (roughly) at the time the exploratory packet was being flooded through the network. This gives the greatest choice of routes to the receiver, but creates a problem with excessive number of packets being communicated.

To limit circulation of exploratory packets a number of schemes is possible provided each node stores the largest sequence number received for every OD pair. One possibility is to flood the exploratory packet to all neighbors (except the one from which the packet was received) only once - the first time the packet is received. Another possibility is to check the number of nodes the exploratory packet has visited and to relay the packet only if either it has a larger sequence number than the number of the packet latest flooded for the same OD pair, or if it has visited fewer nodes than the previous packet with the same sequence number. This last scheme guarantees that an exploratory packet will be received via a route with minimal number of nodes.

There is a problem if the receiver's response to a VC request never reaches the transmitter because of link or node failures along the chosen route. This can be handled by the transmitter using a time out, and transmitting a new exploratory packet for the same VC carrying, however, a **new** sequence number. Note that the transmitter should have ultimate responsibility for accepting or rejecting a VC connection, and the receiver is passive in this regard.

Finally if a node can crash, and not remember the sequence numbers last used, a scheme such as the one of Section 5.3.2 can be used.

5.36

(a) For small values of r_w the first derivative length of a path is almost equal to $D'(0)$ times the number of links of the path. Therefore a path that does not have minimum number of links cannot be shortest and therefore cannot carry flow at the optimum.

(b) Consider the single OD pair network shown below:

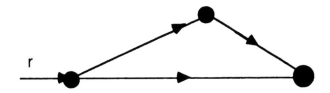

Each link has cost function $D(F) = F + 0.5F^2$. Then, by applying the shortest path condition, it is seen that for $r \le 1$ the optimal routing is to send all flow on the one-link path, but for $r > 1$ the optimal routing is to send $(1 + 2r)/3$ on the one-link path and $(r - 1)/3$ on the two-link path.

5.37

The origin of each OD pair w sends a message carrying the value of r_w along the shortest path for the current iteration. Each link (i,j) accumulates the shortest path link flow

$$\overline{F}_{ij}$$

and sends it together with F_{ij}, D'_{ij} and D''_{ij} to all origins. All origins can then calculate the stepsize α^* of (5.69) and change the path flows x_p according to the iteration

$$x_p := x_p + \alpha^*(\overline{x}_p - x_p),$$

where

$$\overline{x}_p = r_w \text{ if } p \text{ is the shortest path and } \overline{x}_p = 0 \text{ otherwise.}$$

5.38

(a) The average round trip delays on paths 1 and 2 corresponding to x are $T_1(x)$ and $T_2(x)$. These are used to estimate the average number of unacknowledged packets on paths 1 and 2 according to

$$\overline{N}_1 = \overline{x}_1 T_1(x), \qquad\qquad \overline{N}_2 = \overline{x}_2 T_2(x).$$

The actual average number on the two paths are

$$\tilde{N}_1 = \tilde{x}_1 T_1(\tilde{x}), \qquad\qquad \tilde{N}_2 = \tilde{x}_2 T_2(\tilde{x}).$$

Therefore if the routing method used equalizes the ratios

$$\frac{N_i}{\tilde{N}_i}$$

the relation of part (a) must hold.

(b) We assume with no loss of generality

$$x_1 + x_2 = \tilde{x}_1 + \tilde{x}_2 = r$$

$$\tilde{x}_1 < x_1 \qquad\qquad \tilde{x}_2 > x_2.$$

Therefore, by the hypothesis of part (b), we must have

$$\tilde{x}_1 < x_1 \quad \Rightarrow \quad T_1(x) > T_1(\tilde{x}) \quad \text{and} \quad T_2(x) < T_2(\tilde{x}).$$

From the relation of part (a) we have

$$\frac{\tilde{x}_1}{\overline{x}_1} = \frac{\tilde{x}_2}{\overline{x}_2} \frac{T_1(x)}{T_1(\tilde{x})} \frac{T_2(\tilde{x})}{T_2(x)} > \frac{\tilde{x}_2}{\overline{x}_2}$$

Therefore $\tilde{x}_1 > \overline{x}_1$ and, since $x_1 + x_2 = \overline{x}_1 + \overline{x}_2$, we must have $\tilde{x}_2 < \overline{x}_2$.

(c) The vectors x, $\tilde{x}$, and $\overline{x}$ lie on the same line of the 2-dimensional plane, and $\tilde{x}$ lies between x and $\overline{x}$. We now argue that a convex function that has a lower value at $\overline{x}$ than at x must also have a lower value at $\tilde{x}$ than at x

5.39

See the references cited.

5.40

(a) Let D_i^* be the correct shortest distance to 1 from each node i.

Claim 1: Eventually, $D_i = D_i^*$ for all nodes i.

Proof: Assume that $D_i = D_i^*$ for all nodes i that have a k hop shortest path to node 1. Consider a node j that has a k+1 hop shortest path to node 1 of the form (j,i,...,1). This node will receive $D_i^* + d_{ij}$ from i and therefore will have $D_j = D_j^*$. The assumption is clearly true for k = 0, and by induction it is true for all k.

Claim 2: A finite time after claim 1 is satisfied, node 1 receives an ACK from each of its neighbors.

Proof: When claim 1 is satisfied, the set of arcs connecting each node i ≠ 1 with its predecessor forms a directed shortest path spanning tree rooted at node 1. (For a proof of this, see the discussion in the text following Bellman's equation.) Consider a leaf node j on the tree. Each of its neighbors must send an ACK in response to its last distance measurement. Therefore, j sends an ACK to its predecessor. By induction on the depth of the tree, node 1 eventually receives an ACK from each neighbor for which it is the predecessor. Node 1 clearly receives ACK's from its other neighbors as well.

(b) The main advantage of this algorithm over the one in Section 5.2.4 is that node 1 is notified of termination, and hence knows when its estimates are correct. The main disadvantage is that this algorithm requires a specific initial condition at each node, making it difficult to restart when a distance measurement or link status changes.

CHAPTER 6 SOLUTIONS

6.1

The window size required is at least 101 packets since the delay from the time a packet begins transmission to the time its permit returns is 505 msecs. If the transmission time of the permit or the time the permit is delayed at the receiver are nonzero then the window size should be accordingly larger. See the figure below.

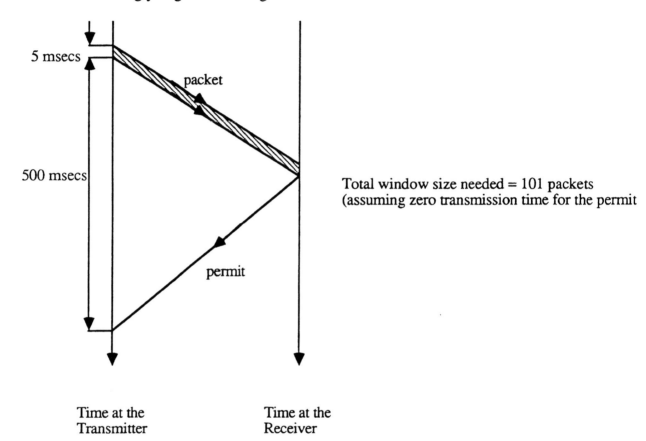

Total window size needed = 101 packets (assuming zero transmission time for the permit

6.2

The Maximum throughput is limited by the transmission rate of the terrestrial link (50 packets/sec). The timing diagrams below show that an end-to-end window size of $\lceil 525/20 \rceil$ = 27 packets is required to achieve full speed transmission in both cases where the terrestrial link comes before and after the satellite link.

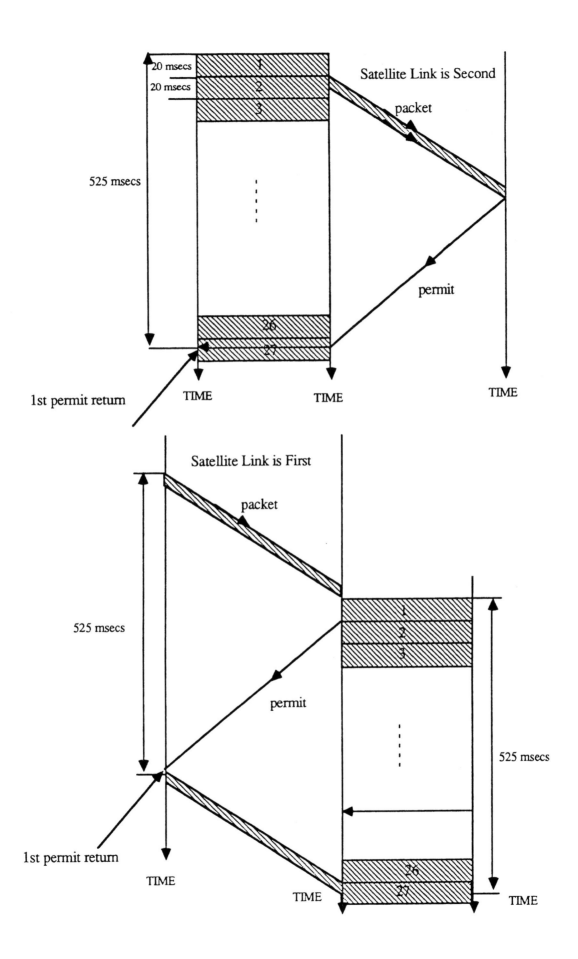

20 msecs

20 msecs

1

2

3

525 msecs

Satellite Link is Second

packet

⋮

26

27

permit

1st permit return

TIME   TIME   TIME

Satellite Link is First

packet

525 msecs

permit

1

2

3

⋮

525 msecs

26

27

1st permit return

TIME   TIME   TIME

6.3

We need a window of at least 1 for the terrestrial link, and a window of at least 26 in the satellite link. If the permit transmission delays are nonzero, larger windows are required for nonstop transmission to be possible.

6.4

See the following timing diagrams:

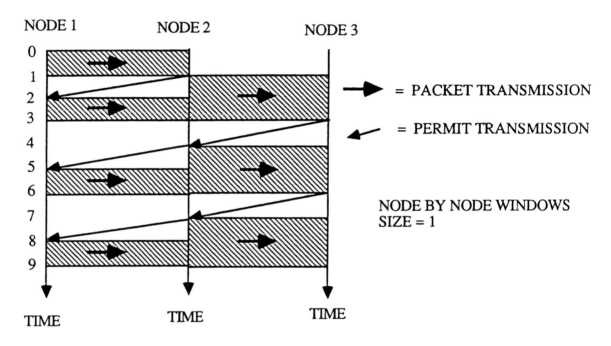

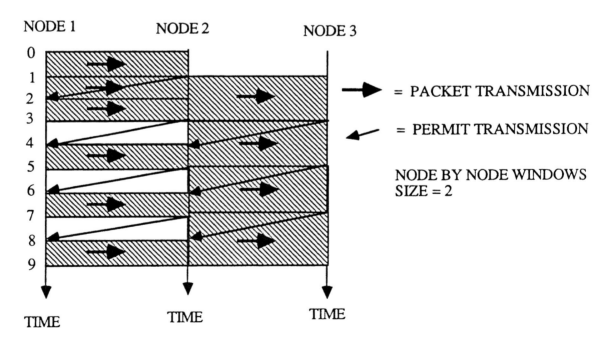

6.5

The following example shows that the alternative scheme requires a larger window, and therefore also more memory. Note also that if link (i, i+1) is a satellite link, the window of link (i-1, i) must also be large if a permit is sent by i after an ACK is received from (i+1). This is not so if a permit can be sent upon delivery of a packet to the DLC.

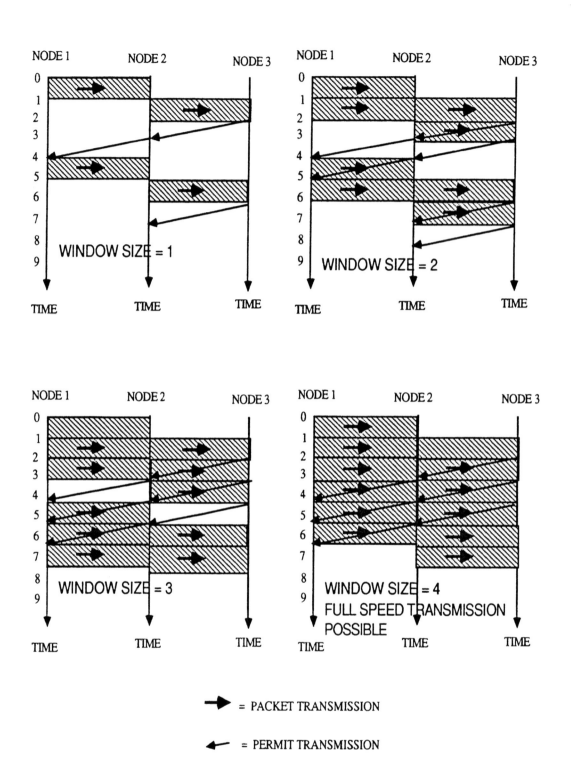

NODE 1   NODE 2   NODE 3

WINDOW SIZE = 1

TIME   TIME   TIME

NODE 1   NODE 2   NODE 3

WINDOW SIZE = 2

TIME   TIME   TIME

NODE 1   NODE 2   NODE 3

WINDOW SIZE = 3

TIME   TIME   TIME

NODE 1   NODE 2   NODE 3

WINDOW SIZE = 4
FULL SPEED TRANSMISSION
POSSIBLE

TIME   TIME   TIME

= PACKET TRANSMISSION

= PERMIT TRANSMISSION

6.6

The augmented network including the overflow links for the two OD pairs is shown in the figure below:

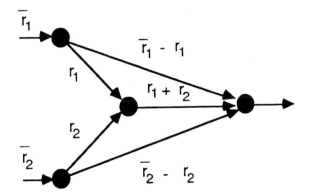

Consider three cases:

a) $r_2 < \bar{r}_2$, $r_1 < \bar{r}_1$, b) $r_2 = \bar{r}_2$, $r_1 < \bar{r}_1$, c) $r_2 = \bar{r}_2$, $r_1 = \bar{r}_1$.

Case a): By symmetry here $r_1 = r_2$. The optimality condition is

$$2r_1 + 2(r_1 + r_2) = a/r_1^2$$

which implies $r_1 = r_2 = (a/6)^{1/3}$. This case is in effect for

$$(\alpha/6)^{1/3} < \bar{r}_2 = 1$$

which yields $a < 6$.

Case b): Here the optimality condition is

$$2r_1 + 2(r_1 + \bar{r}_2) = \frac{a}{r_1^2}$$

or equivalently $4r_1^3 + 2r_1^2 = a$ which can be solved for r_1. This case holds for

$$6 \le a < 4\bar{r}_1^{-3} + 2\bar{r}_1^{-2} = 4{,}200$$

Case c): This case where no flow control is exercised holds for $a \ge 4200$.

6.7

The number of sessions for each network link are shown in the figure below:

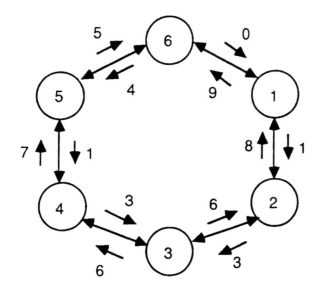

NUMBER OF SESSIONS ON
EACH LINK SHOWN NEXT
TO THE LINK

There are nine counterclockwise sessions and they all go through arc (1,6). At Step 1 this arc is saturated, and the rate of all counterclockwise sessions is fixed at 1/9. At Step 2 of the algorithm arc (4,5) (the one that carries the most clockwise seesions) is saturated and the rate of the sessions going through it is fixed at 1/7. There are only two sessions (5 to 6 and 3 to 4 clockwise) that don't go through this arc. At Step 3 the arc (3,4) becomes saturated and the rate of session 3 to 4 (clockwise) is fixed at 2/7. Finally at Step 4 of the algorithm arc (5,6) becomes saturated and the rate of session 5 to 6 gets fixed at 3/7. The solution is now complete since the rate of all sessions has been fixed.

6.8

For each session p add an artificial node p and a link from p to the entry node of the session having capacity b_p.

6.9

(a) The Markov chain is shown in the figure below. The state gives the session and the order of arrival (and also transmission) of the packets in link L. Note that because the permit delay of the session B packets is zero, there are always two packets from B in link L. All transition probabilities for a small interval δ are $\delta + o(\delta)$ corresponding to a unity transition rate. To see that the steady state occupancy probability is 1/10 for every state verify that these probabilities satisfy the global balance equations. This is seen from the fact that there are as many transition arcs coming into each state as there are going out. The total steady state throughput is one packet/sec which is the transmission rate of link L. The steady state throughput from session A is 0.4 because only 4 out of 10 states correspond to transmission of a packet from A, while the remaining states correspond to transmission of packets from B.

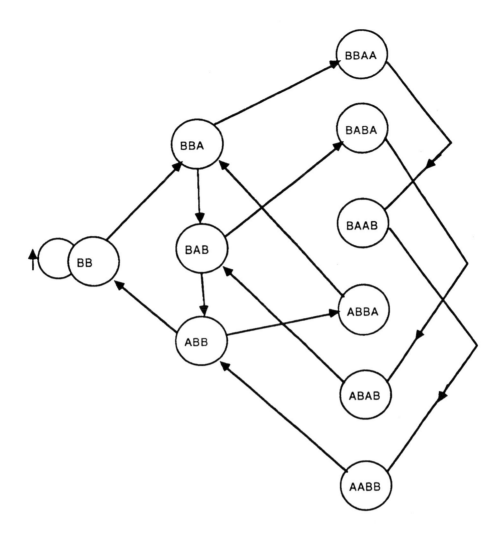

(b) The state transition diagram is given below. The state is the triple

(number in L from A, number in L from B, session currently transmitting)

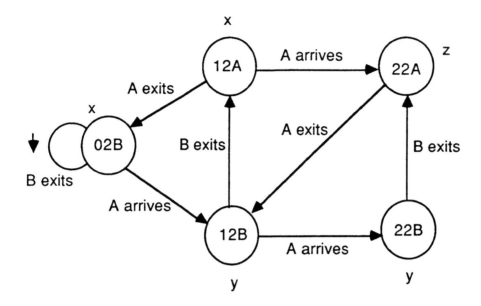

All transitions have unity rate. Applying the global balance equations to states (02B), and (22B) we see that

steady state prob. of (02B) = steady state prob. of (12A) = x

steady state prob. of (12B) = steady state prob. of (22A) = y

Let

z = steady state prob. of (22A)

Applying the global balance equations to nodes (12B) and (22A) we obtain

$$x + z = 2y, \qquad z = x + y$$

Combining these equations with $2x + 2y + z = 1$ we obtain

$$x = 1/9, \qquad y = 2/9, \qquad z = 1/3.$$

A transmission of a B packet is completed from states (02B), (12B), (22B) with rate 1, while a transmission of an A packet is completed from states (12A), and (22A) with rate 1. Therefore the ratio of throughputs for B and A is

$$(x + 2y)/(x + z) = 5/4$$

The throughput of the entire system is 1 since there is always a packet from B to transmit on link L. Therefore the throughput for A is 4/9 and the throughput for B is 5/9. Note that this throughput allocation (corresponding to the round robin discipline) is more fair than for the case of part a) (first - come first - serve discipline).

(c) The state transition diagram for the nonpreemptive priority case is given below. The state is again the triple

(number in L from A, number in L from B, session currently transmitting)

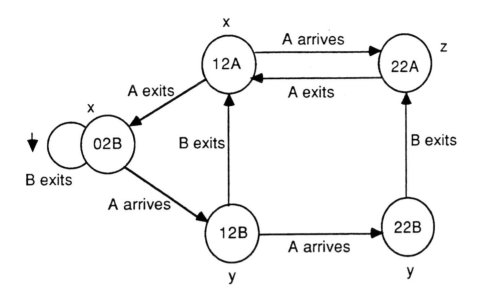

All transitions have unity rate. Similarly as in case b) we see that

steady state prob. of (02B) = steady state prob. of (12A) = x

steady state prob. of (12B) = steady state prob. of (22A) = y

Let

z = steady state prob. of (22A)

Applying the global balance equations to nodes (12B) and (22A) we obtain

$$x = 2y, \qquad z = x + y$$

Combining these equations with $2x + 2y + z = 1$ we obtain

$$x = 2/9, \qquad y = 1/9, \qquad z = 1/3.$$

A transmission of a B packet is completed from states (02B), (12B), (22B) with rate 1, while a transmission of an A packet is completed from states (12A), and (22A) with rate 1. Therefore the ratio of throughputs for B and A is

$$(x + 2y)/(x + z) = 4/5$$

Again the throughput of the entire system is 1. Therefore the throughput for A is 5/9 and the throughput for B is 4/9. As expected, the throughput of A increases over the previous cases since A is now given priority.

6.10

(a) Let state i (i = 0, 1, 2) denote the number of permits available at the source. Then, for small δ the Markov chain for successive δ intervals is given below

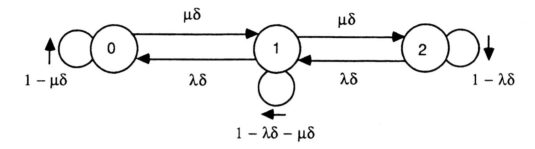

(b) The steady state probabilities are found from $P_0 + P_1 + P_2 = 1$, $P_0\mu\delta = P_1\lambda\delta$, and $P_1\mu\delta = P_2\lambda\delta$. The probability that an arriving packet will be discarded is

$$P_0 = \frac{1}{1 + \frac{\mu}{\lambda} + (\frac{\mu}{\lambda})^2}$$

(c) The probability of a discard increases as delay from source to node (and/or node to source) is taken into account. This is easy to see as the delay becomes very large, since then the permits are very slow to return to the source and almost all source packets are rejected. Analytically, this is not hard to establish for exponentially distributed delays.

(d) A buffer at the source simply adds states to the Markov chain above. Let B_i be the state where there are i packets in the buffer but there are no available permits. The corresponding Markov chain is shown in the figure below. It is seen from the figure that the probability of an arriving packet finding the buffer full is

$$P_k = \frac{1}{1 + \frac{\mu}{\lambda} + (\frac{\mu}{\lambda})^2 + \ldots + (\frac{\mu}{\lambda})^{K+2}}$$

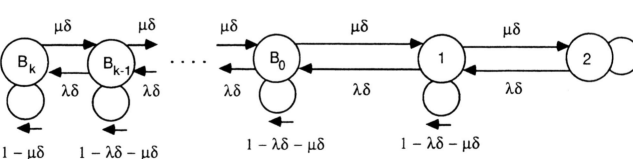

6.11

(a) Suppose that the protocol has worked correctly up to a time t (e.g. the initial time), and at that time the source knows that the destination is awaiting a packet n. Then, for a window size W, the next acknowledgement to be received by the source should distinguish between whether the destination is awaiting packet n, n+1, . . . , n+W-1 or n+W. If the modulus m exceeds W then these possibilities can be distinguished. If $m \leq W$ then the source can be confused. Thus the protocol works correctly for $W \leq m - 1$, and incorrectly for $W \geq m$.

(b) The window size W is no longer restricted by the modulus m. The source can determine the number of the packet being awaited by the destination by counting the number of modulo numbers contained in the acknowledgements.

(c) The destination does not need to know the window size W to perform its part of the protocol. Therefore, the source can change the window size without prior agreement from the destination. However, for the scheme in (a), the window size is still restricted by the modulus.

(d) If the destination delays acknowledging the last packet it has received until it receives the next packet, 1 unit of the window size W is held at the destination and from then on the number of packets sent by the source but not yet received by the destination can be W - 1 at most. Thus the window size can, effectively, be reduced.

6.12

(a) In the memory of node i at any one time there can be at most 2 packets destined for node j that have arrived at node i via a particular incoming link of i, or from a particular external site connected to node i. If the number of links coming into node i, and the number of sites connected to node i that can carry or send packets destined for node j is $n_{j,i}$, then in order to guarantee that every arriving packet for j can be placed in a buffer, node i must have $2n_{j,i}$ packet buffers for packets destined for j.

(b) This scheme constrains all packets with the same destination to use the same link outgoing from a node at every node in the network, thus using paths from a spanning tree. Therefore, not all routings are permissible. Also if the routing changes the buffering scheme ought to be adjusted. Furthermore the scheme is unfair to sessions that go to unpopular destinations. The scheme has the advantage that the required buffering at node i is determined by the degrees $n_{j,i}$ of the node rather than by the potentially large number of sessions that use the node.

6.13

Three rules are needed:

a) At the time a VC is established no permits should become available to the transmitting node of each link on the VC's path.
b) A permit that cannot be used by a VC because no packet is available to send should be returned to the receiver (perhaps after a time out).

c) A node should keep track of the number of outstanding permits it has sent to the transmitter nodes at the other end of its incoming links. The strategy should ensure that this number times the maximum packet length should not exceed the amount of free storage available at the node.

6.14

For full speed transmission the window size W of each session must satisfy $WX \geq d$, where X is the packet transmission time at the origin node of the session and d is the round trip delay. If the trnsmission capacity is increased by a factor K, X will be decreased by a factor K. If propagation delay is dominated by transmission delay, d will also be decreased by a factor K, so the window size of each session should not change. However, the total window size will increase by a factor K, since the total number of sessions is increased by a factor K.

If transmission delay is dominated by propagation delay, d will not change, so the window size of each session should increase by a factor K. The total window size will then increase by a factor K^2, since the total number of sessions is increased by a factor K.

6.15

The formulation as a Markov chain is similar to the case considered in Section 3.1. The states and their interpretation does not change. In particular, the states are 0,1,..., and for i = 0,1,...,W, state i corresponds to W-i permits available and no packets without permits waiting. The states i = W+1, W+2,..., correspond to i-W packets without permits waiting and no permits available. However, the state transitions occur at the times 0, W/r, 2W/r,..., just after a set of permits arrives. The probability of k packets arriving in W/r seconds are

$$a_k = \frac{e^{-\lambda W/r}(\lambda W/r)^k}{k!}.$$

The transition probabilities are as follows:

$$P_{io} = \begin{cases} \sum_{n=0}^{W-i} a_n & \text{if } i \leq W-1 \\ \\ a_{i-W} & \text{otherwise} \end{cases}$$

$$P_{oi} = \begin{cases} \sum_{n=0}^{W-i} a_n & \text{if } i \leq W-1 \\ \\ a_{i-W} & \text{otherwise} \end{cases}$$

and for $i \neq 0$ and $j \neq 0$,

$$P_{ji} = \begin{cases} a_{i-j+W} & \text{if } j \leq i+W \\ 0 & \text{otherwise} \end{cases}$$

6.16

We assume here that the desired OD pair input rates are known, and that each node knows all link cost functions, and its own input rate penalty function. The simplest distributed scheme that can be used is for the links to broadcast to all nodes the values of their total flows (using a flooding scheme for example). Then each node can execute the gradient projection iteration and change accordingly the values of its path flows and the flow on its own overflow link.

6.17

Suppose there are three nodes 1, 2, 3, and two links (1,2) and (2,3), with capacities 2 and 4, respectively. Consider three sessions with paths

$$p_1 = (1,2), \quad p_2 = (2,3), \quad p_3 = (1,2,3).$$

The max-min fair rate is

$$r_1 = 1, \quad r_2 = 3, \quad r_3 = 1.$$

If session 1 is eliminated, the new max-min fair rate is

$$r_2 = 2, \quad r_3 = 2.$$

If the capacity of link (1,2) is increased to 4 units, the new max-min fair rate is

$$r_1 = 2, \quad r_2 = 2, \quad r_3 = 2.$$

Thus by reducing the load of the network either by eliminating sessions or by increasing some link capacities the **minimal** rate will not decrease, but not necessarily all the rates.

6.18

See the second reference cited.

6.19

(a) Suppose i is backlogged in some interval $[\tau,t]$. Then for each j,

$$\frac{T_i^{l_i}(\tau,t)}{T_j^{l_i}(\tau,t)} \geq \frac{r_i}{r_j}.$$

Summing over j

$$T_i^{l_i}(\tau,t) \geq \frac{r_i(t-\tau)}{\rho(l_i)} \qquad\qquad (*)$$

Thus a session i backlog of size q is always cleared in q/r_i time units. Now letting $Q_i(t)$ be the size of the backlog at time t, we obtain

$$Q_i(t) = A_i(\tau,t) - T_i^{l_i}(\tau,t) \leq W_i + \left(r_i - \frac{r_i}{\rho(l_i)}\right)(t-\tau) < W_i$$

where the last inequality follows from the assumption $\rho(l_i) < 1$. Finally, since session i backlogs are cleared at a rate greater than r_i, it follows that a bit is never backlogged for more than W_i/r_i time units.

(b) Since Eq. (6.11) holds at each link it follows that $(*)$ must hold as well. Thus the guaranteed backlog clearing rate over the session i route is

$$g_i = \min_{l \in L} \frac{r_i}{\rho(l)} = \frac{r_i}{\rho_{max}^i},$$

where L is the set of links traversed by i. Now if session i is backlogged in at least one link during the interval $[\tau,t]$, then since we are ignoring propagation delay and the traffic is perfectly pipelined, it follows that

$$T_i^{l_i}(\tau,t) > \frac{r_i(t-\tau)}{\rho_{max}^i}.$$

The bounds on delay and backlog follow directly from this fact.

(c) This problem can be solved analogously to parts (a) and (b). The key observation is that when $g_i \geq r_i$, we have at link l_i (the first link traversed by session i)

$$T_i^{l_i}(\tau,t) \geq g_i(t-\tau)$$

during all intervals $[\tau,t]$ that session i is backlogged at link l_i. By reasoning similar to part (b) we see that this property holds at all links traversed by session i. Thus there are never more than W_i bits in the network, and no bit spends more than W_i/g_i time units in the network.